# Two Weeks in the Trenches

## REMINISCENCES OF CHILDHOOD AND WAR IN ERITREA

## ALEMSEGED TESFAI

Translated from Tigrinya by the Author

**The Red Sea Press, Inc.**
*Publishers & Distributors of Third World Books*

11-D Princess Road   **RSP**   P. O. Box 48
Lawrenceville, NJ 08648     Asmara, ERITREA

# The Red Sea Press, Inc.

*Publishers & Distributors of Third World Books*

11-D Princess Road    P. O. Box 48
Lawrenceville, NJ 08648    Asmara, ERITREA

Book and Cover Design: Roger Dormann
Cover Art by Mikael Adonai

Catalog-in-Publication Data available from Library of Congress

ISBN 1-56902-168-8 (Hard cover)
ISBN 1-56902-169-4 (Paperback)

# CONTENTS

**Introduction** ...................................................................................v

**Early Writings and Childhood Memories**
Shobere.................................................................................3
Grazmatch Tsegu .................................................................13
Hansu ...................................................................................25

**In the Field of Battle**
Two Weeks in the Trenches.................................................43
At the Battle of Afabet: The Drama of a Piece of Flesh...........99
Heart of *Tegadalai*............................................................129

**Plays—Life in the Camp of the Enemy**
*Le'ul* ...................................................................................139
*The Other War* ...................................................................167
*The Other War:* An After word ..........................................211
Glossary ...............................................................................217

Dedicated to the memory of
Temesgen Haile, friend
and
Mebrahtu Tewelde, brother
who both gave their lives for freedom.

# Two Weeks in the Trenches

## An Introduction

### By Dan Connell

*Two Weeks in the Trenches* is good, solid, riveting history. But it is also literature. The language is gripping, the translations are excellent, the material is compelling. It is informative, but it is also deeply rewarding beyond its surface subject matter.

This collection makes an important contribution to Eritreans everywhere who are anxious to better understand what lay behind the liberation of their country. It is also a window on Eritrea's remarkable freedom struggle for others who want to know this, including those like me who were there off and on throughout the war but not this close to the action on any systematic basis.

But Alemseged Tesfai uses these experiences to ask bigger questions and address wider issues. What is it like to live under an authority, internalized in the very personalities of those who rule over you, that erases your identity, that denies your basic humanity? What is genuine heroism, and what motivates it? How does war, all war, debase us, and how can we rise above its corrosive effects to retain our capacity for compassion and for self-knowledge?

This book relates a narrative of pain and humiliation, both personal and political; of abiding strength and indomitable courage, also at once personal and political; of wrenching decisions large and small forced on people by the terrible conditions in which they lived and died; of shameful cowardice and mind-bending heroism in the face of these epic circumstances—in short, of Alemseged's and Eritrea's long and difficult journey to liberation.

These pieces showcase Alemseged—Eritreans generally go by their first names—as a writer of diverse talents and insights on many levels. This is no mean feat for any author, but it is especially unusual for one coming out of a political culture of personal silence, where individuals do not make a practice of revealing what goes on within their movement, their unit, let alone their person. In this and other respects, *Two Weeks in the Trenches* represents a breakthrough that we can only hope other Eritreans will follow.

The stories and essays also reveal a lot about Eritrean culture, as do the plays, even as they recount key moments in the national struggle waged by the Eritrean People's Liberation Front. The Afterword to "The Other War" is especially interesting for what it says about Alemseged as a colonized person and future freedom fighter. But where does the courage and strength come from to do what these fighters do, he asks in the lengthy essays that make up the core of the collection. His early stories provide a partial answer.

"Shobere" is a coming-of-age tale, constructed in terse prose with no fluff or flab, just the raw and immediate experience of youth confronting adult authority—and learning from it. Several boys are caught in the act of inattention in their elementary school class, one of the more common "crimes" that pre-adolescent boys everywhere commit on a regular basis. In rapid succession, we feel the hurt, the humiliation, the holding back of tears, and the bravado with which boys bull their way through such encounters. But there is more.

The initial episode leads the children through a series of incidents that teach fresh but abiding lessons on the abuse of power, the dangers of mob action, the liberatory character of collective resistance and the surprising sources from which respect for self and others can grow.

In "Grazmatch Tzegu," we are introduced to a gentle but mysterious wheel-barrow pusher and to the puzzle of how a person may fall in status but not in stature. This is another coming-of-age story with a twist, valuable as much for the fact that the puzzle itself is not resolved as for the fact that it is grappled with at a tender age with a sensitivity that presages much of what the adult freedom fighter will face later with the same reflective intelligence.

The third of the childhood reminiscences, "Hansu", provides youthful insights into the cruelty and hypocrisy of self-absorbed and insensitive adults even as it takes us on a journey through tragedy and comeuppance that reveals the potential of self-knowledge to carry us through adversity. Here is another lesson of profound importance for one who will spend much of his adult life in the agony and intensity of a protracted liberation war to which most of the world paid scant attention until the dogged strength of a people who refused to be subjugated shocked us with a stunning final victory. How they got there is the subject of much of the rest of this collection.

The title essay, "Two Weeks in the Trenches," is an extraordinary account of fighters on the frontlines during one of the most spirited and difficult defenses of the movement in Eritrea's 30-year war for national liberation. This and the complementary essay "At the Battle of Afabet" provide a fascinating firsthand view of how the EPLF operated, who its leaders were and how they functioned, how battles unfolded and more, but it is also a continuing examination of Alemseged's journey to self-knowledge.

A large part of what makes these stories so interesting is that they shine the spotlight on the supporting cast of characters in this human drama—not only the women and men who led the struggle, but the mostly anonymous fighters whose strength, courage, ingenuity, and steadfastness were the EPLF's secret weapon. The descriptions of these people and places are vivid and convincing and far more complex, even contradictory, than one might expect in such nationalist narratives.

\*\*\*

It is 30 July 1985. One minute Alemseged is drinking *suwa* and singing revolutionary songs with his comrades in the EPLF's Information Department. The next he is slogging through the darkness at full speed across the harsh volcanic terrain of the Sahel Mountains to witness—and at times to participate directly in—the battle to repulse Ethiopia's last sustained military offensive of the long and bitter war.

Once at the front, he finds that the fighters are so close to the enemy that they toss stones at the opposing trenches to determine if anyone is there before advancing. Behind the lines, these fearless combatants sing and dance with the same fury they carry into battle. "Last night I watched them jump, swing, scream and shout in some of the most profound expressions of contradictory feeling that one could ever come across," writes Alemseged. "What kind of people are these?" To the extent that such questions have answers, he sets out to find them. And to relate his discoveries to us.

For these freedom fighters, personal courage has become the stuff of daily existence. It is taken for granted. Martyrdom, he finds, is embedded in the EPLF's political culture. No one expects to survive. They do not speak of what comes after the country's liberation, only of the certainty that this day will come and that future generations will share in its bounty. This motivates them to fight on.

But where this account transcends its genre is where Alemseged tells us what a typical day is like among such heroes and such heroines—for there are many remarkable women peopling these pages—during moments where their mettle is not being tested in combat. He tells what they eat and drink, how they tease each other relentlessly, the jokes they play on each other, the sports they take up to relieve the tension, the generosity they express toward one another, the loss they experience when a comrade falls, the struggle they go through to suppress such sentimentality in order to survive—and to fight on. And he does this with compelling personal anecdotes that make what might otherwise sound forced and barely credible seem commonplace.

There are night patrols and forced marches. There is a terrifying trek through an unmarked minefield—terrifying to the reader, anyway, though hardly more than unsettling to the fighters who do it.

Even when several do not make it. Alemseged continually struggles to comprehend this fearlessness—what he calls the fighters' "disdain for death." Yet he is himself grazed by a tracer bullet during a battle and charges forward with the others as if it is no more than a flea bite.

However, for all this, Alemseged does not romanticize the carnage around him. In the midst of one combat account, he steps back to reflect on the fundamental horror of what is taking place, and he tries to imagine what was going through the minds of the Ethiopians his fellow fighters were mowing down.

"The cruelty of war has no bounds," he writes at another point, after losing a close comrade. "That night I hated not only the oppressor who was the cause of all that, but also those who had invented the murderous weapons of death and destruction that were flashing, burning and exploding right below me."

\*\*\*

In "The Battle for Afabet" we get a blow-by-blow chronicle of the March 1988 EPLF offensive that turned the balance of forces in favor of the Eritreans and led to total victory three years later. This was the fight that won the war, and we get to see how and by whom it was done as we follow key combat units through the rout of Ethiopia's notorious Nadew Command.

Alemseged is a combat reporter for this campaign, and he travels with frontline soldiers to observe the action. In the process, he gives us several revealing portraits of the commanders who executed what was clearly an extremely well-thought out battle plan—people like Mesfin Hagos, Adhanom Gebremariam, the late Ali Ibrihim. We watch them respond with aplomb and intelligence to opportunities that arise as the fighting unfolds, all the while staying within the basic operational objectives laid out with precision and confidence in advance of the attacks. And we get vivid insights into their distinctive personalities as they calmly bark out orders. "Are you slicing and peeling them from their positions?" asks 85th Division commander Witchu, as his forces advance. "Just keep slicing and peeling."

At the same time, we are taken inside the egalitarian political culture that the EPLF painstakingly developed among its members, none of whom, even the top commanders, carried overt signs of rank or privilege. The unusual mix of individual brilliance and collective esprit that this engendered helps to explain the movement's remarkable successes on the battlefield. It also carried with it the potential for a different kind of nation after the smoke cleared over a newly independent Eritrea. But, notes Alemseged, the strength and the character of these unsung heroes as well as their suffering and loss and their inner wounds all need to be better grasped for this potential to be realized.

"Our revolutionary culture is still very poor in discussing and describing individuals and individual acts of courage and heroism," he writes. "Unless we do that, the *tegadalai* [freedom fighter] will never get his due, his or her greatness will never be known. We keep using very general and lofty terms to define the collective. One hears about perseverance, tenacity, grit and fortitude as characterizing the spirit of *tegadelti*. I find such words extremely limiting and an obstacle to describing what the life of *tegadelti* constitutes. There is no life in them, no pain...And pain in all its forms, the process of overcoming or suppressing it is what makes the *tegadalai*. True, the corpses in front of me were the result of the unflinching courage of my comrades, the courage to jump into the lion's den and tackle him by hand. What about the pain, though? The deaths, the fears denied, the hatred for blood, the compassion even for the enemy?"

* * *

In "The Heart," Alemseged reflects on the meaning of revolutionary war, as well as the phenomenon itself, and on the character of the people who wage it. And in the plays that follow, written in the EPLF field in the mid-1980s, he explores the destructive experience of living under colonialism—how it eats away at basic human relationships, undermines identity, turns its victims into bitter reflections of those who oppress them. How choices are forced upon us in such situations, how some rise to them and how others do not, how the best of us—the true patriots, the genuine human beings—find the self-knowledge and the strength in discrete but crucially reinforcing comradeship to challenge and overcome these forces.

In the dramas that close this collection and in the overtly autobiographical Afterword to "The Other War," Alemseged takes us full-circle, back to the insights and understandings with which he began this tortuous journey toward self-discovery and collective wisdom. It was impossible, he tells us, to separate ethnicity and politics during the bitter years of occupation and war. It was the utterly unremitting arrogance, cruelty and cynicism underlying not only Ethiopian policy but also character that drove him and thousands of other Eritreans into the liberation struggle. But, he insists, the harsh and dehumanizing responses that such behavior tends to produce cannot be what defines the nation which emerges from it—is not what he and others fought so long and hard to achieve.

Says Alemseged of the character of the EPLF freedom fighters in "The Heart":

> [T]his is a heart of mercy and forgiveness—a heart, indeed, that does not spend sleepless nights in gnawing plots of hate and vengeance. Obviously, it does not want to see repeated even on its enemies, the pain and ordeal it has had to suffer. Nor would it covet from others what is not rightfully its due. The world has yet to recognize this heart that so willingly sheds all that it possesses for peace among men and women. As to the powerful of our age who are intent on crushing it for the success of their own global strategies, I say that they do not understand its nature. Or, possibly, they are deluding themselves.
>
> For, this is a heart that is capturing their weapons and even men with their own weapons. Indeed, it is a heart that has raised its head to defy their awesome power for one quarter of a century. And, like the piece of flesh and the symbol of courage that we found resisting the scourge of the morning sun, it will not be long before the mighty accept that the heart of the tegadalai is not about to disintegrate or to burst out of existence even when trampled on. That they have not done so till now, that they are not pausing to listen to its beat, is a waste....

And, he adds,

> A heart without a guide may prove fickle and flighty, and we will need to cultivate, expand, educate and wisen it. A product of the people, it was nurtured by the people. In return, it has shed tears of blood for them. It has fallen for their sake. It is, therefore, incumbent upon this heart to tune its beat with theirs, to preserve their culture and protect their honor, to understand their problems and seek solutions for them. It has the obligation to approach them, not from an attitude of superiority and disdain, but with modesty and humbleness. Above all, we have the duty to guarantee that it renews its oath and lives up to it's responsibility never to assume the role of dispenser of freedom and ride over its own people.

History alone will judge whether and to what extent these lessons, these hard-won insights, endure in this specific situation. But the experience that undergirds them and the vision thus generated remain a beacon for all who love liberty and equality and who cherish the common humanity of those who yet strive for them.

Asmara, February 2002

# EARLY WRITINGS AND CHILDHOOD MEMORIES

# Shobere

I was nine or ten. Grade 4A had an English teacher whom we simply called The Teacher. There were thirty-three of us in that class.

One day, The Teacher was correcting our class work. As usual, we were standing in neat lines between our rows of desks. It was a weekly affair that we enjoyed. It gave us the chance to stretch our legs and make a little noise. The Teacher would call us to his side and correct our exercises in front of us. If he was pleased with the result, a terse, "Back to your seat," was the reward we got. If he was not, he would push us away or a knuckle would land on each head. It depended upon his mood of the moment.

Tekle and I shared a desk on the front row near the window. The door was across the room, to our right. The Teacher had placed us there for direct control. We were, I suppose, considered among the noisiest and the naughtiest, but Tekle had a major advantage. His front teeth were so big that they were rarely covered. No one could normally tell whether he was smiling or plain serious. "Don't laugh at us," we would say to him whenever we wanted to tease him. That would provoke his nasty revenge. He would crack a joke in class and when we would laugh and be punished, his habitual grin would simply be passed by.

On that particular day of the corrections, Tekle and I had been returned to our seat when he touched me on the arm and pointed to the wall on our left. I looked up. Two flies were lying there, one on top of the other. That, of course, was an amusement we could not pass. Forgetful of The Teacher's eyes, I turned around and pointed the spectacle to Ghebrehiwet. Ghebrehiwet was the kid who sat immediately behind me. His skin was beautifully dark and oily. So was his hair, jet-black and straight. His well-arranged teeth were snow-white in contrast. When he saw the flies, he broke into a big smile. All three of us started rocking with laughter.

Suddenly, Tekle kicked me on the leg. I turned to him. He had already changed his laughter into a silly grimace and was looking up at The Teacher. Ghebrehiwet and myself did not possess Tekle's expertise in facial gymnastics. So, when The Teacher, who had been watching us all along, stood before us, we were still laughing and stealing glances at the wall. The Teacher looked at me sternly and then at Ghebrehiwet before turning slowly towards the wall. The damned flies did not even care what trouble they were getting us into. They were still joined together in blissful harmony.

The Teacher did not say a word. When he started to walk back to his seat, I knew that we had committed one of the greatest sins in the book. He picked up the stick that he always placed right behind him under the blackboard. "You, come," he ordered me, as he sat on his chair. My heart jumped. Like the man who walked to eternal damnation for having trespassed all Ten Commandments, I approached him with the fear of the unknown.

Throughout the week, I had been showing off a safari jacket that my older brother had outgrown. I had it on that day. When I stood beside him, The Teacher pulled me by the sleeve and shook me a little. "Bend forward!" he shouted. The "ward" was louder than the rest of the command. His word was the word of God. There was no alternative to obeying. Nevertheless, I pretended not to have understood and, hoping that my jacket would ease the force of the impending blow, I bent backwards, letting my coattails dangle between the stick and my buttocks. With incredible speed, The Teacher grabbed me by the neck, forced me to a stooping position, pulled my coattails over my back and swung his stick. It was expertly executed, for it landed on the upper extremes of the back of my two thighs. The pain was excruciating.

Crying did not go well with The Teacher. You cried only if you wanted a second blow. With my whole body aflame, I felt one sharp bullet of a pain shooting through me, towards my eyes. If it had managed to get there, the tears would have flown. But, I caught it at the throat and walked back to my desk speechless, tearless and miserable. I hated Tekle with all my soul, I did not even look at him. I just fidgeted on my seat.

"Ghebrehiwet!" called The Teacher. Whenever he wanted to frighten people, he would stress every syllable of a name. Poor Ghebrehiwet, he was not even troublesome. He went without so much as a slight hesitation. "Bend down!" With no argument, resistance or pretension, Ghebrehiwet bent forward. The inevitable blow followed immediately. The sound was different from mine. Mine was sharp, like a clap. Ghebrehiwet's was duller, more like a thud or a knock.

As was his habit, Ghebrehiwet came back smiling. I was still in pain and unable to sit properly. I needed some sympathy, at least a silent exchange of mutual suffering with Ghebrehiwet. So, I turned back to look at him. Ghebrehiwet's eyes were bloodshot, his muscles taut and his dark, oily face drained of the usual luster and radiance. He was a shocking sight. He did not even give me any time to scream for help. His head dropped on his desk, his body slid towards the aisle to the right and sprawled unconscious on the floor. Later, we were told that he had been hit at the lowest tip of his vertebrae, right on the tail.

Our oldest was thirteen, the rest of us barely ten. Everyone screamed in terror, some clambered to the top of their desks. "Back to your seats!" came the chilling command, which was obeyed immediately.

"Tekletsion!" called The Teacher. Tekletsion was our monitor. He was the oldest or the biggest in class 4A. 'Get help, carry the child outside and pour some water on his head," ordered The Teacher, still sitting on his chair.

Tekletsion and another sturdy kid from the backseats carried Ghebrehiwet out of class. As far as most of us were concerned, he was dead. My child's imagination even went further and I pictured myself attending my first funeral ever. The prospect was so exciting that I added to my adventures. With the funeral over, I saw

Tekletsion, Tekle and myself avenging Ghebrehiwet's murder. As the hero of the action drama, I was performing some incredible wrestling feats when The Teacher's voice bought me back to 4A.

He was leaning out the window to my left and talking to the guard. "How is the boy?" I heard him ask.

"He is fine, Teacher," came the guard's voice. " When we poured water on his head, he came back to life. But, he is limping."

"Tell him to walk home very slowly. He is excused for the day." He closed the window and went back to his corrections.

Every one in our class loved Ghebrehiwet. So, I was happy that he was still alive. I admit, however, that I was disappointed for having had to miss that exciting funeral. I also wanted to continue the drama in which I had been starring so effectively. I thus let Ghebrehiwet die for the moment and went on with my frightening acts of revenge. That afternoon, The Teacher died several times from judo kicks and knockdown blows, only to be brought back to life for more deaths and suffering. It was an exhausting experience.

* * *

Anyone who thinks that children do not hold grudges is mistaken. We hated The Teacher throughout that week. Fear was added to hatred when we saw Ghebrehiwet limping and unable to play for several days.

The Ghebrehiwet incident must have had an effect on The Teacher as well. Many of us noticed him raise his hand for the usual knuckle on the head or a slap on the face, but uncharacteristically lowering it meekly. That was strange and encouraging. We started to feel at ease in his presence. Some of us even made a pass or two at mischief, just to test the ground, just to see how subdued The Teacher had become. This, however, did not last long. One morning, it was disrupted.

He was reading to us from our English textbook, translating a story into Tigrinya. It was the tale of Mrs. Blackie, the mother of a swarm of baby mice whose husband had been devoured by a cat. The Teacher was a great orator with a strong voice. We were listening to him rapt and spellbound. "Poor Mrs. Blackie," he was reading, "with all her babies she needed help."

He paused for affect and looked at us. He could see that we were enjoying the story. All his sins seemed forgiven. We wanted to hear the end of the mystery. Suddenly, some imp in the middle row said, "Teacher, someone has stolen my pencil." That rascal brought us back from the world of mice to our classroom.

The Teacher could have ignored the complaint. He must have believed the boy, or maybe The Teacher was looking for an excuse to go back to his old aggressive habits. I don't know. "Who took his pencil?" he asked.

No one replied. He threw the book on the table. "Come now. Whoever stole that pencil, come forward and place it on this table."

Still, no reply. He picked the stick from beneath the blackboard and started playing with it menacingly. In the meantime, he was examining each and everyone of our faces. His eyes seemed even more bloodshot, more inflamed than ever.

"Pick the thief from amongst yourselves. Pick him out or you are all thieves!" We were thunderstruck. For us, at the time, stealing was the greatest of all the sins and "thief" the worst of insults. I guess we had not discovered the other transgressions. We were too scared to object. At the same time, The Teacher's accusation was impossible to swallow. We stole furtive looks at each other. Two kids in the third row were already crying.

The Teacher must have read our dilemma. He proposed a solution to the impasse. "All right," he said calmly, "Tear pieces of paper from your exercise books and write down the name of the person you suspect stole that pencil."

A collective sigh of relief filled the classroom. Pieces of paper were immediately torn off our English notebooks. With no shred of evidence against the potential victim, and without even verifying if the pencil had actually been stolen, most of us gave our verdict. Three or four of the oldest submitted blank sheets. All the rest of us pointed to the same person.

Our logic was simple and clear. In those days, kids who frequented teashops were regarded as tramps. "Don't go with that boy. Someone saw him in a tea shop," was a common parental warning. Well, our suspect, Ande, was such a child. He used to hangout in a popular tea joint in town. For this reason alone, he was voted the thief.

When the pieces of paper were tallied, all eyes, including The Teacher's, fell on poor Ande. He sat there, numb and bolt upright. His face devoid of expression, he was staring at the blackboard and weeping. I had never seen so many tears flowing down a person's face. His cheeks were all wet.

"Stand up!" came the well-known pre-flogging shriek. Ande got up and started to approach The Teacher. But the man was in so much hurry that he landed a stick on Ande's shoulder. Four or five more blows followed in quick succession. No one dared come between them. Desperate, Ande rushed towards The Teacher and forced himself between his legs for protection and pity. But The Teacher kicked him away and broke the stick on the poor kid's body. He must have gone berserk, for after kicking him some more, he lifted Ande from where he had fallen, and dropped him out the open window close to me. Luckily for Ande, the window had a height only of one meter and a half.

The cat could never have scared Mrs. Blackie's children the way The Teacher scared us that day. Eyes and mouths open wide, we just stared at him, incredulous. Even after the bell had rang and he had left, there was total silence in our class.

Suddenly, Tekletsion the monitor, spoke in a loud voice. "How could you accuse Ande without any proof. Did anyone see him stealing?"

For the first time, it occurred to us that we might have made a mistake. Tekletsion pointed an angry finger at the squealer and said, "Maybe no pencil was stolen. Maybe that one lied."

Tekletsion had spoken. All of us turned on the squealer. Someone nearby shouted, "You misled us," and boxed him on the chest. Another one kicked him....Had the arithmetic teacher not come in on time, the squealer would have been killed. We absolved ourselves of the terrible mistake of having accused Ande falsely. "The squealer misled us," became the adequate and liberating explanation.

Over the next few days, the Ande affair was celebrated throughout the school. Tales of his bravery, of how he wrestled The Teacher with the stick breaking on his back, of how he braved the drop off the window...became favorite topics. To ease our conscience and to campaign against The Teacher, we turned Ande into a hero. I remember envying his newly acquired status.

In the meantime, our relationship with The Teacher took a turn for the worse. When children hate, they do so with imagination. We created nicknames for The Teacher. A song was composed about him. Wherever he went, from street corners, underneath bridges and behind trucks, he was called names and whistled at. Although he could not tell which child, there was no doubt he knew it was class 4A in action. Tension developed between us.

*  *  *

Unlike today, we used to attend morning and afternoon classes in those days. One hot afternoon during the Lent, about two o'clock, we were making a lot of noise. The door swung on its hinges violently, traveled 180° and banged onto the adjacent wall. The sound startled us. Chalk dust rose from underneath the blackboard.

"Everyone kneel down!" The Teacher ordered rushing straight to his stick. Like recruits in a training camp, we kneeled next to our respective desks immediately. Without uttering a word and with amazing speed, The Teacher made the rounds to land his stick on each one of our thirty-three heads. Since dodging meant a second blow, Tekle and I, who were last in line, waited for what seemed an eternity.

"Stand up!" We did. "Sit!"

No one even thought of looking at the other. We knew that we were suffering from the same pain at the same time. My scalp was one region of pain. I touched it with my hands. It had swollen right in the middle. Tekle was looking at his hand and crying. There was blood on his fingers.

The Teacher put the stick back on its place and stood before us. "From now on, if I hear anything from anyone of you, beware. If I kill you, your blood money is only worth my one month's salary." His eyes were on fire.

He proceeded to teach us, but no one listened. His questions went unanswered. The bell rang. As soon as he left, Tekletsion came up front and said, "We cannot continue like this. Our arithmetic teacher will come right now. After him The Teacher will come back

9

again. Before he does so, we will jump out the window and run away. It is *shobere*.

"But if you make *shobere* the police beat you up," said one. He probably knew what the word meant.

"What is *shobere?*" asked others. Most of us thought it was something to do or eat.

"Just do as I am telling you," said Tekletsion. "Anyone hesitates or falls back will have to deal with me. Even if The Teacher comes to call us back to class, we will refuse."

After The Teacher, Tekletsion was the most feared in the class. But he was also very popular. No one could dribble a football like he did. A thousand dribbles without letting his right foot touch the ground was what made him famous.

No one paid any attention to the arithmetic class. My heart beat through the whole period. Everyone was restless. At last, the bell rang. Our arithmetic teacher left and Tekletsion jumped out the window to start our *shobere*. One by one, we followed him, overwhelmed the guard and ran out of the school compound. There were playing grounds outside. We assembled there.

We had, of course, no idea what we were supposed to do next. We crowded around Tekletsion. Obviously, he too had no notion what else *shobere* involved. After puzzling for a while he said, "Why are you looking at me? Go play!"

Immediately, each one of us gave to *shobere* a different meaning. For Tekle, Ghebrehiwet and myself, it became *Akhudir* or the "donkey-kick". Marbles addicts fished some out of their pockets and started crawling on the dusty ground. Tekletsion collected a crowd of admirers and, to their delight, started dancing gracefully as he dribbled a tennis ball.

I played a lot in my childhood. However, I don't remember any other game arousing or tickling all of my senses the way *shobere* did that afternoon. I suppose that there is an internal glow, an overflow of emotion that only defiance provokes. There is something about revolting against despots, something that inflames one's soul.

"Oh, *shobere* the beautiful," the three of us donkey kickers shouted in unison. At the count of three, we soared high into the sky and sent our respective left feet at one another. I was hit on the jaw,

Ghebrehiwet on the chest and Tekle in the groin. We fell back heavily and simultaneously. At least one of us should have cried. There was no time for that.

"Tekletsion!" We froze as we were. The fallen on our backs and sides, marble-freaks on their knees...turned towards the thunderous voice that had startled us. Tekletsion let the ball that he had just dribbled hundreds of times slide to the side and roll away from him. I don't think that he even returned his raised foot back to the ground. We must have looked like perfect characters in a still life painting.

"Tekletsion!" repeated The Teacher. "Just as you led them out of class, take them back, now! Run!"

The showdown had finally come. In anticipation of an action packed duel between The Teacher and Tekletsion, we sent our eyes towards our leader and hero. What we saw devastated us. Till this day, I cannot figure out the speed with which Tekletsion had reacted to the command. In the split second between the command and our eager glances, we saw that he had already started the run back to class. No force on earth could now stop us. Only at that age is defeat accepted so unreservedly and without a trace of shame, and the rush to school suddenly turned into a contest of who got there first. The Teacher was waiting for us, arms akimbo, in the middle of the street leading to the school. No one dared pass near him. Keeping at least a ten meters distance away from his reach, we just sped into the compound.

After pushing and jostling at the entrance, we finally found our seats. "Ah, *shobere*", whined Tekle. He was missing it already. I did not share his sentiment. I fixed my eyes on the door expecting it to open any moment. The possibility of The Teacher re-entering to order us to kneel down for yet another knock on each head was real and imminent. No one came. Despite the fact that there was no teacher with us, our class stayed totally calm and silent for a full ten minutes. That, of course, was a school record.

Moments before the end of classes, the door opened gently. Contrary to our expectation, the director, not The Teacher came in. He was not angry. Instead, there was a slight smile of amusement on his face. After taking time to look at all of us pensively, he said, "Do

11

you know that what you have just done is forbidden? It is called '*sciopero*.'" Some of us giggled. We thought that the director was mispronouncing *shobere*.

"Whoever is involved in a *sciopero* is normally dismissed from school. Don't do it again. From now on, you have any complaints, come straight to my office." Without adding a word more, without abusing or striking anyone, he left the class.

All in all, our *shobere* had taken about fifteen minutes.

\* \* \*

After many, many years, when I had become a university student, I remember meeting The Teacher by chance. What I still find surprising is the fact that my old classmates and myself never harbored any lasting hatred or grudge against him. Maybe because, in spite of his violence, he was a good teacher; maybe he gave us a sound educational base. I cannot tell now. I saluted him with a great deal of respect and nostalgia. He greeted me with fondness and pride. I never saw him again.

# Grazmatch Tsegu

In the mid-fifties, *Villaggio Paradiso* was a lot different from what it is today. All the villas to the west of the Asmara-Keren road have now totally replaced the government barracks of those days. The barracks had so much space between them that children could run and play at will.

The big building to the east of the road was two separate buildings with a dirt road running between them. These were joined to form the present structure only much later. The dirt road used to lead to a buttons factory half a kilometer away and then on to *Emba Galliano* some distance farther east. The factory was a smelly place where animal bones were crushed and processed to make all types of button. The two buildings I mentioned were actually the monastery of the *Cistercensi* or *Sitawiayn*, a Catholic association of the order of *San Bernardo*. In the same big compound was a small church and a few government houses. We used to live in one of these.

The mid-fifties was a time when every child in *Paradiso* was crazy about Ghilia Mariano, the great Eritrean goal keeper whose actual name was Ghilamichael Tesfamariam. He had a coach called Wedi Libi, whom we used to watch training Ghilia on the roughest of grounds. He would throw balls at the young goalkeeper in quick succession and expect him to dash, swing and swerve to catch them, regardless the height or direction. Every child wanted to emulate Ghilia Mariano. So, bouncing tennis balls against the walls of *Villaggio Paradiso* and flying into the air to catch them was a favorite pastime. Going home with torn flesh and bruised knees and elbows was also a mark of great things to come. We called the game, "Ghilia's acrobatics."

One day, I swung into the sky only to miss a ball I had just bounced against the wall of the *Cistercensi*. It was a bad fall. Spitting dust from my mouth, I started to run after my tennis ball, when a wheelbarrow that I had neither seen nor heard coming tripped me over. After a somersault that even Ghilia might have envied, I came down crashing to the ground. The barrow overturned too. Animal bones of all description—jaws, arms and legs, skulls, ribs and thigh-bones—literally scattered all over me. I rolled away scared and waited for the wheelbarrow man to beat me up.

"Rise, rise, my son, and clean your clothes," came a gentle voice. The tone might have been from one's own father or from a kind teacher. Even at that age, I could not expect it from a wheelbarrow pusher. It sounded refined and civilized, so I looked up to stare at him.

Tall and thin, he wore a hat. His tattered safari coat and his patched khaki trousers were surprisingly spotless. His sandals were equally worn out. Had I been asked to guess his age then, I would probably have put him at around a hundred. I doubt now if he could have gone beyond sixty.

As I got up to dust my shirt and shorts, he bent down in obvious pain to put the barrow back in place. His movements were slow. He collected the bones, re-arranged them on the barrow and, without a word, started to push it down, towards the buttons factory. Our house was some fifty meters from where I had fallen. I followed him up to our gate. The dirt road was full of stones sticking up from the ground. The barrow shook and made a lot of noise as it jumped over them. It was too short for him. He had to stoop way down in order to push it and, as it shook, he seemed to tremble along.

From that day on, most of the kids in the neighborhood started to take an interest on the gentle wheelbarrow pusher who also sold bones. His punctuality was amazing. At close to five in the after-noon, we would expect to hear the sound of the barrow and the bones jumping on it and it would be sure to come. We would then stop our games and accompany the old man halfway to the buttons factory—up to the juncture that led to the *Cistercensi* school. He never seemed to mind. At the edge of the juncture was a huge eucalyptus tree under which he used to take a rest. He never talked to us, but he seemed to enjoy watching us with very kind and appreciating eyes.

There was, however, one peculiarity about him. Whenever he went past the two buildings towards our houses, he would stop and tilt his hat forward so that it covered his eyebrows and camouflaged part of his face. He would then bow his head and, with his chin almost touching his chest, pass the houses totally unrecognizable. It was the older kids who first noticed this. Fascinated, the younger ones simply followed him. We had never seen his type of wheelbarrow pusher.

One day, when most of the neighborhood children had strayed somewhere else, my sister was playing alone. He stopped near where she had been and, as usual, started to work on his camouflage. He watched her long and carefully. A piece of bone had fallen off as he was stopping the barrow. My sister ran over and put the bone back on its place.

"God bless you, my daughter. May you have many children who will run errands for you," he said to her. After a pause, he asked her for the names of our parents. She told him.

"Where are your older brothers and sisters," he asked her next, even mentioning their names. She told him again. Without another word, he left with his face hidden.

My sister could not wait for the rest of us to come. When she told us what he had said, all four of us siblings raced home to tell my mother about this strange revelation from our strange friend. Everyone talked at the same time. Mother frowned till her eyebrows met.

"Who could he be?" she asked. "Why didn't you ask for his name?"

"He rarely talks," we replied.

"What does he look like? Give me an indication. Does he have a scar on his cheek? Is one of his teeth missing?"

"He doesn't have a scar."

"How do you know? You can't even see his face...." We almost

15

came to blows.

"Then who could he be?" Mother kept musing. "A wheelbarrow man who knows your father and my older children!" Mother became concerned.

She was right. This was the fifties and the Second World War was still very recent history. Hundreds of Eritrean family, friends and neighbors who had gone to the Italian campaigns in Libya, Somalia and Ethiopia had not returned. Individuals reported dead and duly commemorated were occasionally popping up; some were being re-reported as still living, married to some "Galla" women somewhere in Ethiopia....One could not give up on the missing. Anticipation, expectation and hope were still in place. Mother had cousins and in-laws who had not come back. Therefore, her concern and interest in the man with the wheelbarrow.

When Father was told about the incident with my sister, he paused to think. He was, of course, not as excited about it as Mother had been. When Mother started to go down the list of names that were in her head throughout the afternoon, however, he got irritated. "And now we are guaranteed a sleepless night," he cried out. "All the people you are mentioning are dead. The date and place of their deaths have been identified. Are you proposing to bring them back form the grave?"

"How about your brother, Woldie? We have not been told about him."

"That's preposterous! How can my brother, Woldie, be still alive and pass by my house, pushing a wheelbarrow?"

"All right then, who is this man?"

"*Non so*," replied Father, reverting to Italian, as he did whenever in deep thought. "If he comes by tomorrow, stop him and ask him. If you recognize him, fine. If not...." He also mused as he rose to go to bed, "What intrigues me is, whoever he is, why such a man would be pushing a wheelbarrow. I just wonder...."

\* \* \*

Probably because there were other areas where he collected discarded bones, my wheelbarrow friend would sometimes disappear for days on end. After the talk between my parents though I had developed my own curiosity about the man and stood on the look-out for him. Four days passed without his appearing. I was about to give up when I heard the familiar sound of the barrow approaching from a distance. I ran home and told my mother that the mystery man was coming.

Our house had a fence thickly covered by bougainvillea. Mother found a hole to see though and waited for him to come close to our house. She then stepped outside and intercepted him. Without look-ing up, he tried to guide the barrow around her and simply pass her by. She blocked him with her body.

"Sir," she said to him, "could you kindly put your barrow down and take a short rest?"

With his hat concealing his forehead and eyebrows and his chin touching his upper chest, his face was invisible to her. Try as she did, she could not see any part of it.

"You know my husband and my older children. Who are you and where are you from?" Mother asked earnestly.

"Let me pass, please. I am a guest. I know no one in this city." His voice was calm. He tried to move on, but Mother blocked him again.

"But you know us. Was it not because you recognized my daugh-ter that you asked her about my family? And who could ever have told you the names of my children? You couldn't have guessed."

"Your daughter told me herself. Now, would you let me move on? It's getting dark and I am in a hurry." There was neither anger nor haste in his voice.

Mother caught a hold of his sleeve and said, "Please, sir, tell me who you are. In the name of God, I beg you to identify yourself. Don't run from your own. Your voice and your structure seem famil-iar. Don't close your heart to the world...." She begged him with feeling and sincerity.

He would not be moved. In attempting to release himself from her grip, he lost some balance and the wheelbarrow almost over-turned. As he struggled to put it back in place, his head turned and Mother got a glimpse of his features. I saw her face brighten up slightly, as if in vague recognition of the man in front of her. She probably saw no purpose in struggling with him any further. She let go of him and off he went shaking and trembling behind his wheelbarrow.

Mother waited for my father's arrival in total silence. She just kept twisting and biting her lips in utter surprise and sadness. "Oh, Chief of all the Saints," she kept calling on her patron saint, St. Michael, "And what are you going to show us next?" She got into an unending argument with herself.

Whenever Mother got into that mood, the best thing to do was just leave her alone. No amount of questioning or persuasion would prompt her to tell anyone what would be on her mind. Instead, we kids would wait for Father to come and, as soon as they started to talk, we would create excuses to enter the dining room one by one and, by arranging the bits and pieces each of us had heard, we would make sense of what was being said. That evening, we got ready for such an adventure.

"I know who he is, it is Grazmatch Tsegu," Mother said even before Father had put his hat on the hanger.

"Who?" he asked.

"The wheelbarrow man".

"Go away! What kind of woman are you? Tsegu disappeared a long time ago. Where would he come from?"

"I am telling you. Big nose, small chin, even his birthmark is still there."

"Are you mad? I am telling you he disappeared. And if he hadn't, how about his land in the village? Who would deny him his ancestral rights? Why would he become a wheelbarrow pusher? Just give us dinner, will you?"

"Why don't you listen to me? How can I ever miss Grazmatch Tsegu? All that friendship, the good neighborliness...I think you should try to find out about him. Something has obviously befallen him."

An argument ensued. All of us kids came out of the kitchen to surround the dining table, where they usually ate alone. They did not even notice. From their exchanges, we came to realize that the mystery man was one whose status did not allow him to be pushing barrows and selling bones. During the Italian period, he had

18

attained the fourth grade, the highest there was in the colony. In the first Libyan campaign, he had been made a *shumbashi,* again the highest rank for anyone, in the Eritrean regiments. He had later become an interpreter for Italian governors, and a friend to Italian *maresciallos* and one of the candidates for the exalted rank of *Dejazmatch.*

"Where did he go later?" asked my older brother.

"In *trenta cinque,* when we went to Tigray in Ethiopia, we left him here in Asmara. Afterwards..." father thought for a while, "After that...I don't know where he went after that. I remember asking about him once and I think they told me that he had gone back to Tripoli. Then he disappeared...or so I heard."

"Well, here he is, pushing a cart right in front of your house." Father's hesitation was reassuring my mother. As she rose to serve dinner, she shuddered at the way fate treated some people and entreated all her saints to distance a similar catastrophe from her family and her home.

\* \* \*

Mother did not give up. She was set on establishing the man's identity. She told me to stand guard and to tell her if I saw him. I was now the official spy and my eagerness to find him and play a part in solving the mystery was second only to Mother's. One afternoon, his familiar figure appeared in the distance.

Mother rushed out of the house and stopped him again. Standing in front of him, she said, "I recognize you now. There's your face, there's your birthmark. I can't ever miss Grazmatch Tsegu."

He lowered the barrow with great care and almost straightened up in full. With his head tilted to the side, he looked at her from under the rim of his hat. "People look like people, madam." he said with a calm, even voice. "I think I told you last time. I am new here and you don't know me. Neither do I know you. I have never even heard the name you are mentioning."

"No, no way. True, it has been a long time—around twenty years now. But old faces and old folks are not easy to forget. I could not mistake you. We've shared bad times, we have drunk from the same holy source and we have buried each other's beloved together. How

19

can I ever doubt your presence? Come, in the name of the Virgin Mary, let us share your problems if you have any. My husband will come soon. Please come in, I will offer you some *suwa*...."

"Thank you, madam. May your respect be rewarded," he replied pensively. "As for problems, would I be pushing carts and selling bones if I did not have plenty of them? But you have mistaken me for another. I am not Grazmatch Tsegu."

"Then who are you? Excuse my boldness, sir, but why would a gentleman like you be reduced to selling bones?"

"You are the gentle one, madam." he said shaking his head and returning the compliment. "But who would know how people fall? Some fall because they are lazy, others because they are inept. Still others get reduced to pauperism because of evil done unto them. And then there are those who give up on the ways of the world to seek the solace of monasteries. A few shun monasteries and prefer to live on the fringes of life, away from humanity. Who can predict the ways of the Lord? Who can ever change it? Our destinies are written. We just come and go."

Mother must have realized that he was not about to confirm her suspicions. As an attempt of last resort, she said, "All right then, swear on my right palm with your right hand that you are not Grazmatch Tsegu. Swear by the cross hanging on my neck, swear in the name of the Creator." She was stretching her palm and touching the cross as she said so.

The trace of a smile lightened his face up. Instead of responding he just gave her a knowing look, re-arranged his hat, lifted the handles of the barrow and got ready to push. Mother knew that there could be nothing more that could be said. She stepped aside to let him pass. With the smile still on his face, he moved out of her sight.

"God be with you, Grazmatch. May the Mother of Christ put her eye on you. How sad, how so tragic..." she kept murmuring as she led me into the house. She walked straight into the kitchen and put a whole *injera* on a large plate. She then spread some *shiro* on it, took a liter of cold *suwa* from her cupboard and ordered me to follow the old man and have him eat and drink her offerings.

I found him sitting beneath the tree at the juncture down the road. He was examining and dusting his hat. I thought the faint

20

smile still adorned his face. Without uttering a word, he folded the *injera* with the *shiro* on it and stuffed it into a bag he always hung on his shoulder. I then filled some of the *suwa* into the tall glass Mother had also given me. He took a sip first and tasted the drink. He then emptied half the contents of the glass without even gasping for breath. He paused, wiped his mouth with his hands, belched and then emptied the *suwa* remaining in the glass.

I offered to pour him some more from the bottle. He stopped me with a motion of his hand. "No, enough, my son. I never drink more than one glass at a time," he told me and, with the usual pain slowing his movements, he got up to go.

He put his hat on, straightened his coat and bent towards the barrow. He took two or three steps forward and stopped abruptly as if he had remembered something. He turned around and talked to me.

"Please, thank your mother," he said. "Tell her she was right. Only old friends and old folks are those who care. Thank her for me once again and tell her that Grazmatch Tsegu is sorry for having disappointed her so." Having said that, he pushed as hard as his age and frailty allowed.

I doubt if I have ever run as fast as I did that day. Excited and breathless, I told Mother what the wheelbarrow man had told me. "I knew it," she said, and let me go out to play. My brother and sisters had to beg me for information. I would not give more than bits and pieces. I killed them with suspense and anticipation.

That evening, Father listened to my report with great interest. "I too asked about him," he said after I had finished. "I was told that he had suddenly distanced himself from all who had known him. He had no family and no children. But I don't think anyone else knows that he is pushing a barrow and selling bones. It is strange, simply unbelievable...." He tapped his fingers on the table.

"Could it be that bad times overtook him?" asked Mother.

"What else could it be? Maybe, as he said, some people intrigued against him. Or it could be something internal, it could be that he could not go in step with these times. Yes, bad times overtook him. I will try to meet him...."

* * *

Father tried to find Grazmatch Tsegu but could not. He even changed the hours he came home, all in vain. The man simply disappeared from our neighborhood. Maybe he always disappeared from neighborhoods in which he was being recognized and that was how he was succeeding in hiding his identity. Maybe he had fallen ill or had died. We could not find out. "Bad times overtook him" became, for us, a phrase ever linked to his name. In time, his name and story started to fade from the collective memory of our home.

I would not forget him though. Why? Why had a man of that background and standing fallen to pauperism? Because he was incapable or lazy? Because, as Father had said, "he could not go with the times?" Could intriguers and plotters have ejected him from his father's land and shut him out of all means of livelihood? Or was there a more profound explanation? Maybe he hated people and despised society.

To this day, I have found no solution to this conundrum. Since all the people who knew or could have known of him have passed away, I have been unable to collect more information about him than this short tribute contains.

A while ago, I went to *Villaggio Paradiso* and toured the former compound of the *Cistercensi*, where we had also lived. I found all our houses leveled to the ground the old garden destroyed and the road closed. The eucalyptus tree at the juncture is no longer there.... It is another place, with very little signs to tie it to my childhood memories. Another world and another time...I took myself away, disappointed.

I left in haste, because the whole scene threatened to spoil my cherished images—the images of play and innocence, the picture of "Ghilia's acrobatics" and the memory of the people of those days, as represented by Grazmatch Tsegu.

Although I was a mere child, I feel I saw in that man great values unshaken and untarnished by adversity and poverty. One is respect—not only respect extended to all regardless of age and status, but also respect for himself and within himself. The other value I saw was greatness. Not the external greatness of birth and appointment, not even that of age, but the internal greatness of spirit and wisdom. That is probably what made him resist dependence on others, what helped him preserve his dignity. Indeed, I believe that that is what motivated him to choose life in the peripheries of society and to reject comfort in favor of pushing barrows and selling bones....

That is why I have not forgotten him, indeed, why I will remember him for as long as I live.

# Hansu

Anyone who would ever say that Hansu is capable of finishing a sentence without giggling is a liar. Any topic she handles, funny or sad, serious or light, is so broken up by chuckles and titters that her points are rarely made. One could, of course, get used to or simply ignore all the cackle and snort. However, her smiles are accompanied by a set of teeth that, to put it mildly, are not that attractive to look at. It seems as if, in their formation, all thirty-two of them had rushed to the front to contend for position and visibility. The result can only be imagined—they protrude so much forward that they almost jump on you when she so much as starts to talk.

For this reason alone, Hansu was considered as one of nature's victims. Her childhood was spent almost solely in the exclusive company of her mother and younger sister. No one else in the village cared to even look at her, much less talk to her. She was a loner. As if to spite her, nature had given to her younger sister, Haregu, the most enchanting set of white teeth, straight hair flowing down to her waist and a heart-stopping charm. Thus, no one had ever doubted that Haregu would one day precede her less endowed sister to the altar.

Hansu's misfortunes did not end there. Her kind father, the only friend and protector she ever had, had gone away to fight poverty, but he never returned. Word had come that he had succumbed to malaria somewhere in the lowlands of western Eritrea. Add orphanage to nature's cruelty, and it had seemed as if Hansu's future was doomed.

To be fair, though, nature had not been as harsh on Hansu as had first appeared. She had been so overshadowed by Haregu's wit and banter that her great talents had largely gone unnoticed. But Hansu was a specialist in braiding and basketry. In her hands, women's hair turned into exquisite embroideries of refined art. Give her plain and tinted grasses, leaves, roots and twigs, and what woman would compete with her in twining, plaiting and coiling them to make perfect baskets of unimaginable shapes and colors? She never tired of grinding flour or weeding chaff; fire and smoke never deterred her from baking the best *injera* in the village.

In short, she was made for marriage and the family. Men, however, are fools. They give to looks more credit than it actually deserves. If someone had closed his eyes to those cursed teeth and protruding lips and had just snatched Hansu away, he would have been guaranteed a capable, faithful and hardworking wife.

But let us not get too carried away. Hansu's fate was a source of worry only to her mother and to close relatives and neighbors. She never seemed to even bother about it—and not, as one might think, because she was self-conscious about herself and had given up on men. Had she been inclined that way, she would not have uncovered her teeth after every phrase or syllable of a word. She would at least have developed techniques of hiding them from constant exposure.

No, Hansu was free from that kind of shrewdness. She was, like her father, open, kind and unselfish. She never knew how to say "No", how not to give. She was of the type that wept more about other people's problems than themselves. She was famous for giving away to beggars what her mother would eke out of the little plot of land the father had left them. If it had been possible, people said that she would not even hesitate to dismember her own arm, to give to whomever needed it more. She was, in short, generous and had not this rare quality brought misfortune upon her, we would have listed it as one of her great merits.

It was the year after Haregu had married a truck driver on the Assab-Addis Ababa road and had gone with him to Ethiopia. It was also the day when her mother and the whole neighborhood had gone to a funeral in a distant village. The midday sun was so scorching hot that even village dogs were sleeping. The village watchman, a man from across the Mereb in Tigray, Ethiopia, chose this moment of slumber to jump over the fence and barge into Hansu's house. He found her sitting in her mother's kitchen, making cheese in a gourd hanging from a rope on the ceiling.

Startled, Hansu let go of the gourd, which swung to and from in mid air. "Are you all right? Why do you come to me through the backdoor?" she asked quite perplexed.

The watchman, who was well aware of Hansu's legendary kindness and generosity, raised his right hand in feigned innocence and said, "I am sorry I frightened you. I had no idea you would be alone. I thought I saw some goats in your backyard and I just jumped in to drive them away and to warn you to look out for them. They can destroy your garden you know."

Kind-hearted Hansu believed him immediately. "Oh, poor man," she said, "You are running around in this heat? You must be thirsty." She mixed some milk and curd into a large tin cup, stirred it carefully and gave it to him to drink. He gulped it in at one go.

By the time the watchman jumped over the fence to go the way he had come, the afternoon had worn out. The villagers were already coming back from the funeral and the cattle from the grazing fields. Everything, except Hansu, seemed normal. Without realizing that she had been committing a grave mistake and, indeed, a sin, and totally forgetting her mother's behest to guard her honor at all and every cost, she had simply given up, squandered may be the right word, her only hope, her only source of dignity.

They say that one moment's error changes a lifetime. They are right. The watchman's seed had born fruit. With the gradual, inevitable transformation of Hansu's body, village gossip grew louder. As the mother's suspicion got confirmed, her despair and abuse turned Hansu's life into one of misery.

Things turned for the worse for the unfortunate girl when the watchman, afraid that he might be forced to marry Hansu, crossed the Mereb and disappeared into Ethiopia. In a village that chose sneers to consolation, rejection to accommodation and curses to forgiveness, Hansu found life totally unbearable.

The baby girl, a rubber stamp of her mother, came in due time. Three months later, Hansu wrapped her up in rags and left the village with only a few coins to get her to Asmara, where she had a rich and learned uncle whom she had never ever seen. She had heard that he was a man of great sympathy and compassion. She went to him in the hope that he might at least understand her ordeal.

The uncle was preparing for a Sunday stroll when she caught him at the entrance of his villa. Child in arms, she kneeled down to kiss his feet while introducing herself. "I am Hansu, your brother Tesfa's daughter. Forgive me, sir," she said as she bent down.

He must have heard of her. He lifted her up by the shoulders and took her in. Sitting on a chair, he looked both at her and her baby daughter and seemed to cringe inside. He had been the first of a family of a dozen children and the only one to break loose from the poverty of the countryside and to attain education and wealth in the city. His hand was tired from a lifetime of giving. A brother whose bull had died, a sister whose husband had left her, a family whom drought had impoverished...would rush to him for help and hand-outs. "These people are ruining my house!" was an everyday lamentation of his wife. That was why he cringed when he looked into the faces of his new guests.

"I cannot just throw my own niece away," he told his wife after withdrawing with her for consultation in the bedroom. "Let her stay here until the baby gets a little stronger...."

"You are not serious, are you? Do you know her? She is a fool, a moron. As if I am not bearing their other problems, are you now asking me to raise their illegitimates? I am not going to keep her. Send her away yourself or I'll throw her out!" His wife of forty years had no doubt her voice would be heard.

Just to test her will, the uncle refrained from taking any step for about a week. But when his warm and comfortable life threatened to turn into one of constant bickering, he gave Hansu some money and took her to the bus station. There he told her that she was to go to Addis Ababa where, he hoped, her sister Haregu or one of his three sons would take care of her. So, Hansu went to Addis Ababa.

* * *

When Haregu saw her sister Hansu on her doorway, a thunder-bolt might as well have struck her. She stood there motionless. Soon after their wedding, her husband had opened a small boutique in a kiosk, from the impressive stock of contraband clothes, perfumes, soaps and cheap ornaments that he had amassed over the years. Haregu was learning how to manage it. The couple had also rented a house with two rooms and a kitchen in Mercato, right in the heart of Addis. In one room was a set of locally-made plastic sofas and a dining table with a few chairs. The bedroom was crammed by a double bed, a cupboard with a full-length mirror and the baby's crib— the typical furniture of the aspiring lower middle class.

Like many before her, Haregu had already started to sprinkle some Amharic words and intonations into her formerly flawless Tigrinya. It did not matter that she did not yet know their exact meaning or usage. She just let herself adopt that manner of speech. She felt that it was making her sound new, elevated and urbane—different from the village girl who had turned her back on poverty barely two years before. She even worked on improvising and perfecting it.

She liked Mercato. All the noise, the hectic movement and the daily mingling of crowds of people with donkeys, carts and motor-vehicles made her forget the loneliness of her village and her mother's hut. As she saw her husband's income increase by the hour, she started to yearn for the day when she would equal her more advantaged cousins. When they all squeezed their sedans and convertibles through the back alleys of Mercato to come and grace her daughter's birthday, for example, she had felt that she had the world in the palm of her hand. She had felt that she stood at least a head or more taller then her envious friends and neighbors. No wonder that she took refuge in Mercato with a purpose and a vengeance.

It was under these circumstances and on a morning when she was smiling happily at life and her little daughter that the child-carrying face and frame of Hansu made its rude interruption. Haregu had not mentioned, even to her best friends, about a sister back home. All they had known of her relations were her dazzling line of cousins. The ghost of her past, a life that she thought she had given her back to and that she had permanently removed from her heart, was now at her doorstep. She froze right where she stood. She saw her worth devaluing and her robust status deflating. As Hansu rushed forward to squeal and giggle and hug and kiss her little sister, Haregu did not respond, even for the sake of appearances. She just wished the bad dream would end.

Late that evening, her husband pushed the door open and strode in with his usual force and confidence. He had his day's earnings from the shop in a bag. He immediately noticed that the furniture in the living room had been moved to one side. He also saw someone sleeping on the floor. Frowning until his eyebrows met, he went straight into the bed-room. Haregu was waiting there to serve dinner.

"Who is sleeping in the other room?" he asked his wife.

"Hansu."

"Your sister? Did I see a baby?"

"Yes."

"Where'd she get it from?"

"She said from someone in the village."

"Oh, God! Men are such beasts. Who in the world would want to…" he interrupted himself, probably out of consideration for Haregu's feelings. "Why is she here?"

"I don't know. She told me our uncle sent her to us."

"Why didn't he take care of her himself?"

"I really don't know," Haregu sounded frightened.

"You don't know? So who's supposed to know? All right, listen. Either send her away first thing in the morning or just get lost with her. I don't want to see her tomorrow night." His trade had taught him to make quick and final decisions. Haregu knew that once set, he would not change his mind. She was despairing.

"I too am not happy she has come. But where can I take her?" she ventured to ask.

"You have cousins who don't know what to do with the money they have. Take her to them and this case is closed."

He ate dinner without uttering a word more. Uncharacteristically, he did not touch her that night. Probably for greater pressure and effect, he went to sleep with his back to her. He did not even see Hansu the next morning. He was gone before she had waken up.

In the following few days, the issue of Hansu dominated the minds of her cousins. With two of them married and the youngest courting a candidate, they got busy calling each other and cursing their father's extended family. What to do with Hansu? Send her back home the way she had come? That would be going against their father's request. Keep her in their homes? Their wives would not hear of it....

"Let's give her some money to see her through a couple of months or so," proposed the youngest. He was the kindest of the three.

"And then what?"

"And then...I don't know. She should try something. She could do women's hair. Didn't they say she's good at braiding?"

"I think that's a good idea," declared the oldest, a man with a big villa and two limousines. "Why don't we make our contributions immediately?" He counted thirty Ethiopian Birr from his pocket and placed them on the table. Haregu had left Hansu in his house when he and his wife were out. Therefore, he had been the most eager to see her accommodated somewhere else.

After a careful search, they found an old and practically abandoned house in a place called Cherqos. Cherqos is situated between Popolare and the Addis Ababa train station. They chose the house not only because the rent was cheap, but also because it was quite some distance from their respective homes. Old blankets, bed sheets, pots, pans and plates and a bed were duly transported into the house. One afternoon, the youngest cousin drove her to her new home.

"So, Hansu, this is your home," he told her. "Here's some money. Be careful how you spend it. You can live on it for two months, at least. From here on to Popolare," he continued sweeping his hands towards the west, "there are hundreds of women from back home in Eritrea. You will make a lot of money braiding their hair. I will show this place to my brothers. We will all come to visit you whenever we can...." His car left a trail of dust as he drove away.

From early childhood, loneliness had always come naturally to Hansu but never had she felt its cruelty the way she did those first few days in Cherqos. In a room that was no wider than her mother's kitchen, in a ramshackle house that she feared would not stand a strong wind, she longed for the misery and alienation of her village. The smell of dung and animal urine that she had grown up with was perfume to her nose, now that she had to cross over everything from the vomit of drunkards to children's defecations in order to get home.

In her simplicity, she had not caught the message that her sister and cousins had passed on to her by their cold reception. She had gone twice to Haregu and once to the oldest cousin in search of solace and comfort. Each time, she had to leave fast and early for fear of being pushed out. She stopped going there but was embittered by their consistent slights.

Luckily for Hansu, Cherqos was a haven for the unfortunate. It did not take long for her to recognize her likes and to make a few friends. The artful hair braids that she had tried on some of them started to get her more clients beyond Cherqos, on to Popolare and even Campo Asmara, far beyond. She became a busy woman. Just as her young cousin had predicted, she was soon earning enough to survive at least from one day to the next. With a firm determination, she patched up pieces and ends to grapple with life in Addis. Her heart had turned sour on her relatives. Eventually, it gave up on them. She would not visit, except for pressing family reasons. Neither was she ever visited.

The years passed by quickly. Her daughter grew up. Hansu could not afford to send her to school. Instead, she taught her every trade in the art of hair braids and plaits. There was a specific style for specific occasions—weddings, holidays, periods of mourning—you name it, she taught her daughter. The giggles were, of course, always there. However, kindness and generosity did not go with life in Addis. She learned how to be more astute and, where necessary, even a little more aggressive.

Hansu was, in short, aging, maturing and growing wiser. Too much hair braiding involves too much bending and tilting. That became a habit and Hansu developed a stoop and a tilt of the head. Her hair grayed. Early each morning, she would lead her daughter out of the house to keep appointments with a line of women. Late in the afternoon, she would buy her daily food from a nearby market and come back home before dark.

In the huge metropolis that is Addis, Hansu disappeared. Addis is a jungle one can hide in. She hid in Addis...almost forgotten by one and all.

\* \* \*

In Popolare, there is an old hotel known as "Guenet". To get to Cherqos, one needs to go through Popolare, to the northeast. One day, a middle-aged woman started crossing the street towards the hotel. Dark in complexion, her hair was neatly braided and she wore a white shawl on her shoulders. A speeding Peugeot screeched as it got close to the woman. There was a bang. The woman was lifted off the ground, fell in the middle of the street and rolled over a couple of times. Her body shook and shuddered for a few seconds and then stopped moving altogether.

As usual on such occasions, passersby, shopkeepers, bartenders and employees and guests of the hotel all ran out to where she lay. Her face had already swollen beyond recognition. "Who is she?" they all asked. "She is a Tigre...have mercy on the poor, lord...." Words of sympathy came from right and left. Spectators who could not stand the sight of blood covered their eyes. Women rubbed their temples with the edges of their shawls as a sign of respect for the dead....

A traffic policeman had already arrived and was taking the usual measurements to determine the cause of accident. As the owner of the Peugeot followed him around, probably to bribe him to his favor, a shrill, loud shriek drew everyone's attention. "*Erre! Erre Gud*, that is Aunt Hansu," came the voice. It was that of a Gurage shopkeeper who owned a kiosk at the edge of the Cherqos market, or the *gulit*, as it is known. "Poor Aunt Hansu," he was already weeping. "She was so poor and so kind...."

The policeman ordered the shopkeeper to call the victim's neighbors. Within half an hour, some of Hansu's friends were covering the body with bed sheets, while others had already gone to inform Haregu and the cousins about the accident. It did not take long for everyone to assemble at the gates of Guenet Hotel.

"It's her," said oldest cousin after a careful inspection of the dead woman's face, "I know, that's Hansu's forehead."

Haregu echoed him word for word and threatened to fall all over the bloody corpse, totally overcome by shock and grief. Her friends had to wrestle hard to hold her from joining her sister on the street.

When the body was sent to the hospital for embalmment, an argument ensued on where it should be laid to rest before burial. It did not take long for all to agree that Hansu's house would be the most convenient and ideal. Five cars, a Mercedes Benz and a Toyota amongst them, lined up to pass through the smelly alleys of Cheqos and to stop near Hansu's dilapidated shack. Someone was told to fetch the body from the hospital.

If the Emperor himself had come, Cherqos would not have been so mobilized and agitated. The whole neighborhood and the whole market ran towards Hansu's house. Cherqos folks—Amharas, Oromos and Gurages alike—stood open-mouthed as they watched beautiful women in tailored dresses and well fed men with neckties and polished shoes cry for Hansu. "All this for Aunt Hansu!" they kept whispering to one another.

Hansu's house had neither a compound nor a porch. There was, however, some space between it and the dirt road that passed some meters away. Fortunately, this was the Lent season, where the sun reigned supreme. Rain would have made the area inaccessible to the types of cars assembled that day. Anyway, some of the cars were sent on errands to bring food, coffee, sugar and other such consumable needs for the week or two of mourning. By mid-afternoon, everything had been put in place for Hansu's funeral later that day.

Haregu was now and again rising from where she had been made to sit, to express her sorrow. She kept half-running from one edge of the assembled mourners to the other, tuning her movements to the rhymes of her sing-song lamentations. Just as her own mother used to do on such occasions, she would point her forefinger to the sky, support her back with her left hand and cry out, "Please, my sister... my own sister... please, forgive me ..." She rocked right and left in uncontrolled regret. In fact, her friends had to rush and hold her hands a couple of times to prevent her from pulling her hair off of her scalp. She was in that extreme a state of remorse.

Soft-hearted woman wept along with her. Some sat in a corner and shed tears in memory of their own long-gone beloved. Others sat unmoved by Haregu's performance. "Where was she till now?" they whispered amongst themselves. "It is too late for regret and remorse...."

"Maybe life was too tough on her. She has many children, you know," ventured the wise.

"Unacceptable," responded the critics.

It was getting late. The body was about to come and the excitement was mounting. Haregu rose for the hundredth time that afternoon and addressed the gathering. "Is that it? Has she left me forever?" she asked between sobs. "Why don't you curse and reject me? I've done her wrong!" She was graying around the temples. She had also lost most of the charm and luster of her youth.

Her husband and cousins crossed over to her once again and tried to reason with her. "We have betrayed her, cousin. We abandoned her..." she said to the oldest. He tried to calm her down gently, telling her that there was nothing that could be done and that God would reward her in heaven. She would not listen. She screamed, pulled out a lock of her disheveled hair and showered words of abuse on herself, her husband and cousins.

They were so upset that they huddled to confer on how best to silence her. As they were talking, the youngest cousin, Haile, was told that someone was asking to talk to him. He moved through the grieving Cherqos crowd and saw the Gurage shopkeeper some distance away. He approached him.

"Sir," said the shopkeeper quite agitated. "Sir, we have made a terrible mistake. Aunt Hansu... she's alive. She and her daughter are waiting for you at my kiosk."

For a full minute, Haile got mixed up in the head. He stood numb and motionless. "Whose body have we been crying over the whole time?" he asked himself as soon as he regained control of his faculties. He also felt a pinch of guilt for not having remembered Hansu's daughter throughout the afternoon. He shook his head violently so he could think properly. Suddenly he started running full speed towards the Gurage's kiosk.

Hansu had no idea why the shopkeeper had almost fainted upon seeing her. He had told her not to move before fleeing away. She and her daughter were sitting and puzzling in front of the kiosk when Haile came running, only to stop stiff some meters away from her. With the ubiquitous large braiding needle sticking between her own braids, she glanced at her cousin. He just stood there in a state of shock.

"Are you both all right? Why am I frightening you so?" she asked standing up. She walked over to greet Haile. She giggled, of course.

"You are alive?" asked Haile. He realized immediately that it was a stupid question to ask.

"What else can I be?" she responded kissing him.

"You did not pass by Guenet Hotel about noon?" Another foolish question.

"No. What's happening here?"

"A lot has happened. I'll come back to both of you. Stay here. Don't move." He ran back at the same speed. Hansu and her daughter looked at each other, more puzzled.

As Haile pushed onlookers to enter the circle of mourners, Haregu was still wailing. "Don't forsake me," she was saying, "Come back to me for one moment. Give me the chance to repay you...." Haile threw a disdainful eye at her, as he approached her husband and the brothers.

It was their turn not to believe what he told them. It took quite a few whispers and furtive glances for them to calm down. Their main fear was that they may soon be entrusted with some stranger's body. They sent strict instructions to stop it from leaving the hospital morgue. The rays of the setting sun were focusing on all four of them. It highlighted their dazed and nervous movements.

"Let's tell them. Let's shut that woman up once and for all," proposed Haile.

"You just saw Hansu. You know more about this. Why don't you tell them," replied the oldest. A man of status, he wished to avoid embarrassment.

"But, you're the oldest," Haile objected. "Besides, you're the one who recognized her by the forehead, remember? I'll go fetch Hansu." He did not even look back. He disappeared behind the crowds and ran to the kiosk.

Haregu must have suspected something was afoot, for she fell silent in order to follow what was going on. When her big cousin moved towards the center of the circle, she started to scream once again. He clapped his hands and said, "May we have some quiet, please. Haregu, please, be silent."

"How can I keep silent...I'm burning inside...."

"Shut up!" he raised his voice in anger. Haregu obeyed. He surveyed the gathering with his eyes and seemed to be at a loss as to how to start. He cleared his throat, rubbed his hands together and began to speak.

"It looks as if today's tragedy will have a happy ending," he began self-consciously. All eyes turned to him. Haregu cocked her ears. "It is a happy ending, but, honestly, it is also very embarrassing. Today, we made a terrible mistake. The face was unrecognizable. The body that we sent to the hospital was that of a stranger. In other words, we are waiting to bury a woman we do not know. Hansu is nearby. My brother will bring her here presently."

Total silence and stillness followed the speech. All attention, however, turned on Haregu. Her eyes had remained transfixed on her cousin's face throughout his talk. They remained there even after he had resumed his seat. She frowned to concentrate, and to try to make sense out of the weird turn of events. She seemed to realize that she had said much, too much in fact to her liking. As if she had not been pleading for one chance of atonement, she appeared afraid of its imminence.

Suddenly the spectators to all the drama moved to open the way to the Cherqos market. Not even priests carrying the altar could have evoked so much awe and respect. Haile appeared first. With a smile that could not hide his embarrassment and discomfort, he led Hansu into the middle of the circle of mourners and onlookers. The silence and stillness grew even heavier.

Hansu stood there for a full minute, glancing right and left. As was her habit, she lifted her left hand and pressed the braiding needle deeper into her knotted hair. At last, she spoke, "Well, here I am! Are you going to bury me alive?" And she gave a giggle and a chuckle.

"She's right, what's the matter with us," shouted one of her neighbors. "Let's welcome her, women. Let's ululate," and she let out a shrill and loud ululation.

The silence broke. People started to rush towards Hansu. Some kissed her cheeks, some shook her hands, while others pulled her by her dress and shawl. She felt overwhelmed, even congested and cluttered. Never had she been the object of so much attention, so much concern. At first, it unnerved her; later, she withdrew into herself, and just stopped responding.

"Open the way, let her pass," she heard people say. Haregu's face appeared from among the crowd. The shawl was still tied tightly around her waist. With her swollen eyes avoiding Hansu's gaze, she stood in front of her. After some hesitation, she went down on her knees to prostrate herself at Hansu's feet.

"Forgive me, my sister. I have wronged and abandoned you. Please, forgive me."

"Oh, no. Don't do that, for the sake of God." Hansu pulled Haregu by the sleeve, attempting to make her rise. "Get up, please, my sister...." Haregu lifted her head and they gazed at each other. No words came out of Hansu's lips. Her face was unusually serious. Her whole body was shaking from the emotion she could not control. She felt as if her legs and knees were about to betray her. After appearing to swoon a little, she slumped on the nearest chair.

The Cherqos crowd had seen enough. Their daily routine of poverty and stagnation had now been broken by an item of interest that would dominate *tella* house gossip for some time to follow. They left for their respective homes, and to the marketplace. Hansu was soon alone with her daughter, her sister and her cousins. She stayed where she sat, totally lost in her own private thoughts and feelings. She seemed remote and unapproachable.

"Hansu," said the oldest cousin attempting to ease the tension, "Why are you so pensive? Why aren't you happy as we are? We had completely given you up you know."

Her weary eyes shot a glance at him and, probably for the first time in their existence, her teeth uncovered a sarcastic smile. "This is not the first time. You gave me up a long time ago." There was no reproach or self-pity in her voice. It was just a statement.

The cousin had not expected the response. He fidgeted in his chair and gave an inaudible grunt. He looked like he wanted to say more, but the words would not come. He turned to the others for help.

The brother-in-law stretched his long legs and cleared his throat for attention. "Well," he ventured, "That's why your sister, myself, all of us are asking for forgiveness. We want to compensate you for our past mistakes...."

Hansu gave him a side look and said, "But I have been compensated already. If I had really died, Cherqos would have witnessed the most impressive funeral ceremony in its memory. I am content that I was so honored at least in death. Can I ask for more? I have, indeed, been repayed and there is nothing to forgive."

Hansu, whom they expected to giggle and cackle through the incident, was throwing bitter and piercing words at them. They had no idea how much her lonely and painful life had transformed and hardened her. For those few moments, they hated to even look at each other. They scratched their heads, plucked at their mustaches or simply fiddled their fingers in nervous reaction. Haregu dug into the earth with the soles of her sandals in silent contemplation.

Haile was the only one who looked amused by Hansu's new found sharpness. His voice full of admiration, he pleaded with her, "Listen Hansu, everything you said is true. That's why we are all regretting our neglect of you. We have feelings of guilt right here." He pounded his chest emotionally and continued, "We want to help you. Move from this house, find a better one. We will pay the rent." Everyone nodded in total agreement.

Hansu pressed the braiding needle and secured it deeper into a knot. She smiled. "Haile, my brother," she replied—her voice was now a steady monotone—"I honestly, would not mind the help. But it is coming too late. It is coming after the worst has passed. My daughter has grown and she has become my main support, my backbone. I am not complaining anymore. As for moving from here? Where can I go from Cherqos?" She paused for a moment, appearing to hesitate. She then shook her head and looking up, changed her tone to one of defiance. "No," she declared, "if the worst comes, I'll prefer to go back home. Cherqos embraced me, I can't leave it. But, thank you all. It is getting late."

There was no more to be said. One by one, they stole away into their cars. Haregu paused over Hansu only long enough to say, "I'll come to see you. You too, please, come to me." She did not wait for a reply. She left hurriedly.

About the hour when she had been scheduled to be buried, Hansu and her daughter were left to their old life of solitude in the ruin that was home to them. After the excitement of the afternoon,

Cherqos, too, went back to its usual evening of calm, sometimes interrupted by drunken laughter and song.

Early the next morning, Hansu stuck her braiding needle in its usual knot at the back of her head and crossed Cherqos to make the rounds of her clients at Popolare. Her neighbors greeted her with a great deal of respect and some awe. Proud that she had not betrayed her likes and companions in misery, she too gave her respects to them with grace and dignity.

Deep in her heart, she knew that she would never forget the day when she had been so honored and recognized in public.

# IN THE FIELD OF BATTLE

# Two Weeks in the Trenches

## Notes from a Diary

*3 July 1985*

Tuesday night, July 30th 1985, was an evening of entertainment at Arag, strong *suwa,* beautiful atmosphere, songs, laughter and plenty of dancing.

By 2 A.M. I had had enough and, as always on such occasions, I stumbled against pitch darkness to find my room. I may have tripped-over a couple of times. I don't remember, but the lump on my left knee has no other explanation. Anyway, I found my room, my underground shelter actually, and was soon drowned in drunken sleep.

I had not slept more than an hour, when the sound of fingers snapping close to my ear startled me to a groggy state of awakeness. Finger snapping is a military signal to the sleepy, indicating approaching danger or a call to guard duty.

"What?" I cried out and for the moment I had no idea where I was.

"Line up at the cafeteria. Don't forget your gun," came the reply. Whoever it was, he was gone before I had fully woken up.

I groped in the darkness for my jerry can, poured water on myself with my clothes on, found my pistol and labored my way back to the cafeteria. Many had already lined up under the big tree that we called "the cafeteria". A few die hard drinkers were still gulping last drops from tin cans....

Haile Menkerios was telling everyone assembled that we had to walk all the way to Anberbeb. Once there, we were to be told where we were destined to go. Anberbeb is a good four-hour walk from Arag.

The spirit of *tegadelti* especially in the face of a challenge is difficult to describe, much less to explain. Death and adversity are expected and accepted as ordinary happenings in the normal course of things. So, any call to active duty, regardless of its nature, always creates such excitement that reluctance is rarely encountered. The sick try to hide their ailment and the lazy are suddenly motivated. This is the norm.

When we lined up at the cafeteria, Beshir was told to stay behind. He was not going. He had been wounded on the leg in an earlier battle and was severely handicapped. A man of all trades, he is useful in the everyday chores of the Department. He had to stay behind to take care of the other disabled, the mothers and their children. He raised hell, refused to move from the line and had to be given a final military command to submit to authority. Zekarias is the oldest in our number. He is also constantly bothered by some chronic illness. He too begged to march with the rest of us but was made to stay behind. As we started our march, he stood by the side, sad and dejected, waving us Godspeed and calling for victory.

The excitement of this unexpected march to our yet unknown destination had apparently relegated the power of *suwa* to some lower levels. So, the first hour of our walk passed without any noticeable incident. Luckily for us, the sun was completely hidden by a sheet of cloud and a gentle breeze kept us all almost fresh. But, as we approached Halibet, which itself is half way to Anberbeb, the *suwa* inside most of us started to boil over.

Halibet is at the foot of a steep mountain that we call Bidho, which literally means "Challenge." It got its name from the road carved out of its slopes and escarpments by the engineering and manual skills of *tegadelti*. With thirty-six hair-pin twists, it served the EPLF as the sole lifeline for many years after the Ethiopian army had encircled its forces on the mountains of Sahel. For us, Bidho was more of a killer last Wednesday than a lifeline.

Looking up at it from the flatness of Halibet, the artist Michael

Adonai just gave up and crouched underneath a shrub and refused to budge. As we started climbing Bidho, our neat and orderly line started to disintegrate. Alcohol is mean when it hurts. As I let one foot follow the other in a snail-speed crawl upwards, I tried to ignore the sound and smell of vomit in front of me. Estifanos Dagnew and Teame Beyene, friends from my pre-revolutionary days, were marching close by. This was a test that especially my peers and myself could not afford to fail. I envied the younger ones, "the children of the revolution", as we called them. Many of our internal worries never seemed to bother them. Hakli, Michael Adonai's friend and competitor in art, just sat on a rock and simply said, "Go on, I'll catch up with you guys." Someone tried to help him up, but he refused. "Go man, it is not as if we are attacking a garrison right now." He stayed behind.

One learns quite a few things in a revolution. Succumbing to fatigue, for example, always turns out to be something to regret. For want of a few seconds of perseverance, many have fallen just a few meters from a water well or a final destination. Such occasions often provide fertile grounds for nicknames and hilarious banter.

Although totally spent and with my head pounding with every step I took, I just continued with those terrible and ever-increasing extra few seconds. Oromo and Almaz were the first to scale Bidho. Tesfai Berhe and Ukbai amazed me. They had volunteered to cater to our needs on the way to Anberbeb. I saw them climb up, down, up again and down again that wicked precipice. Like all of us, they had had their fills of *suwa* and had danced all night. But they were neither sweating nor stumbling. I envied them and, frankly, I also resented their energy. I was that tired and that meanly disposed as a result.

It took us about five hours to arrive at Anberbeb, the HQ of the EPLF at the time. A fresh breeze at the top gave some life back to us. We found water in one of the Anberbeb streams and, like small children, just splashed ourselves in uncontrolled joy. All my fatigue was gone. I felt reborn, I could not believe it. Hakli and Michael were the laughing-stock, until a car was sent from Anberbeb to fetch them up Bidho. Their youthful surrender had gotten the better of our grown-up sensitivities. They laughed at us!

We did not stay long at Anberbeb. All fifty of us and some more from the other departments of the base area were crammed on top of an N-3 Italian truck and were soon bumping towards Nakfa. Nothing new happened on the way there just the usual jostling for space in which to move or stretch, a curse here, an argument about someone else's foot there...one of the rare occasions in our revolution when God is remembered and called upon to intervene and bring Nakfa closer.

Nakfa is dry, no rain and no water these days. Everyone from Arag was placed at Embalko the day before yesterday. This is the place where freshly married couples enjoy their honeymoon. Scores of rooms just enough for two to sleep in are dug underground or carved out of hill-sides. Mass marriages and a mass honeymoon take place here whenever the guns are silent at the front line.

Embalko was fun in a quiet way. We were all from the same department, so there was no problem communicating. It felt like Arag, collecting firewood, preparing food and, later in the evening, singing and coining proverbs.

Kirbit was the life of the group. He claims that the ELF had abducted him from his family and raised him isolated. He also says that he had seen some terrible things in their prison. He looks barely 16 or 17 to me, although he claims to be older. Some of the stories he tells are hard to believe. But, he is sharp and he likes to play and tease anyone around him. He paints, plays music, and also writes poems. His constant quips and pranks kept us entertained for two days. He dangles dead rats by the tail and chases the girls...

Not just Kirbit, but several kids about his age are always a pleasure to be with. The spirit of youth is just incredible. I often ask myself if I ever was like them in my youth. Maybe because there was no revolution when I was their age? Could it be because I was not influenced by what existed? I don't know but I try to rationalize. Whatever the case, these are a different breed. Almost every *tegadalai* accepts martyrdom as an inevitable outcome of his or her love and loyalty to country and cause. But, our youth go far beyond that. Some of the Arag kids actually grew up in Sudan as street-boys. Last year about this time, we were all complaining and despairing about their total disregard for discipline and their aversion towards any kind of work. Today, they have changed. Especially now that they are about to go to the place of their dreams, the frontline, and they are not even looking back. Boys and girls, they are all the same.

Yesterday, we were told to assemble under a shade, just outside Nakfa. A brigade commander, Fitsum Wedi Memhir, addressed us. I took some notes.

"Our military situation is dominating even our political activities," he said. "So, we are being compelled to call to the frontline, even those of you who have been undertaking other important organizational tasks. The enemy in insisting that his last drop of blood be shed at Barentu. He has thus gathered forces there and is making continuous attempts to capture that town. We, on our part, have to make all necessary preparations in order to shed those last drops of blood. You have come here as a backup force for the comrades who are standing firm at Barentu. When this is over and we all return to our respective places, every one of us must make sure that he or she has made a piece history. We should not go back ashamed or with our heads bowed down. We should brace ourselves for this short, but bitter period of time...just a few days. Is there anyone who is not ready?" There was laughter and clapping for a reply.

There is no end to the mountains and ravines, the rises and falls of the Nakfa terrain. We left Nakfa behind us, to the southwest, and proceeded towards Sulfur. Sulfur is a mountain whose trees and rocks have literally burned to ashes from persistent bombardments by the enemy—hence, "sulfur", denoting crumbled rock and ashes.

Yesterday I spent the night with the commander of the battalion to which I have been assigned, Haileab Manjus, meaning Little Haileab. He is a person I have known since 1974. I saw him at a place called Sebirseghi when I was first recruited. He was one of Issayas Afewerki's younger aides. He may have been 15 or 16 at the time. We talked for quite a while, mostly about the military situation. I was impressed by his perceptiveness and maturity.

This morning Haileab assigned me to one of the companies at Sulfur. I have mostly been writing and idling around most of the time. Nothing particular to say about today. I am at the office of the company commander.

**4 August 1985**

I am still at the office of the company commander. All of my friends from Arag are gone. I am alone here. Yesterday, I accompanied Bahre Debbas, the company commander, to see the trenches. There is no enemy on the other side. It looks like he has abandoned the left wing of the Nakfa Front. Members of the platoon that I stayed the day with spent a lot of time throwing rocks at enemy positions below, just to make sure that he had evacuated the trenches. There was no response. Some shot at known enemy positions and even exposed themselves to provoke some reaction. Still, no response.

In the afternoon, part of the company went down to the opposing trenches and made a more through search. No enemy. Obviously, his intention is to reduce as much force from this front as possible and to concentrate larger troops in Barentu.

It is amazing how close to each other the confronting trenches were at Sulfur. In some positions, the distance may have been as close as twenty meters only. Anyway, no enemy this side of the Nakfa Front.

**5 August 1985**

We left Sulfur late yesterday evening. We arrived at Kertset about 2:00 in the morning.

It was a rough and bumpy trip—quite exhausting, as far as I was concerned. Our company was first at Kertset. The other two companies of the battalion were arriving one platoon after the other. I was still looking for a spot to lie on, when I heard someone strum the *krar*. In no time, firewood was fetched from all corners and a fire was lit near the *krar* player. A woman's voice filled Kertset's darkness and the *krar* was soon going wild in rhythm to the clapping and dancing of some men and women from our company. It was a Tigrinya *guaila*, which the other companies also joined as they arrived, such that the small gathering quickly grew into a huge circle around the flickering light that also developed into a bonfire.

With sweat from the trip still dripping down their foreheads, their faces glistened on and off with the jumping flames. With an old jerrycan serving as a drum, they all clapped and sang, while they took turns in twenties or thirties, circling the fire in one of the most spectacular Tigrinya dances I ever encountered. As the drum went dum-du-dum...dum-du-dum...the dancers twisted, turned, bent and straightened, each giving his or her own meaning to every beat, rhythm and movement.

The dance of the *tegadalai* is just not an ordinary dance. It is an expression of something deep—of youthful desires unfulfilled, of suppressed joys and sorrows, of dead comrades not openly mourned and of loves not consummated. It is a dance of young men and women with a burning love of country and people, about to pay for that love on the altar of self-sacrifice. Every trip could be a trip to a battle, and every battle could be the last one, as, indeed, every dance. Yet, paradoxically, every trip, every battle and every dance is also a step towards the ultimate goal of freedom and, therefore, one of hope, although one may not live to see it. So, last night, I watched them jump, swing, scream and shout in some of the most profound expressions of contradictory feelings that anyone could ever come across.

Kneeling to remove stones from underneath the sheet that was to be my bed for the night, I shook my head in quiet amazement. "What kind of people are these?" I uttered aloud, mainly to myself.

The Political Commissioner for the company, Wedi Ghile, was also clearing some stones nearby. He must have overheard me. "This is the *guaila* of relative peace," he said to me, raising his voice so I could hear him over the shrieks and thumping some meters away. "You should see them dance after a battle. They bury their dead, tend to the wounded and, at the first chance of some rest, it is *guaila*. They erase their sorrow through dancing. Martyrdom has become a culture."

I want so much to explain this phenomenon, but I have to understand it fully. I doubt if I ever will. It just is not enough to say, "They do what they are doing because they are fighting for their freedom." One has to dig deeper into the roots, the origin. We need to study the life and deeds of the heroes of the past,

How is heroism inherited? It must have its own ways, its own processes. An invisible network of veins and threads must be pumping and connecting it from one generation to the other. True, the EPLF has an official and regulated program of political education that attempts to streamline its membership into one broad outlook. There are also regular sessions of criticism and self-criticism that supposedly place deviants in line. These may serve as a base, but I don't think that they alone can go to the battlefield and create heroes out of ordinary mortals. No, there must be something more fine, something less political and more human in the whole phenomenon.

Whatever it is, kids in their late teens and early twenties have turned courage into a norm. Death is being defied as if it is just a hurdle to jump over, as if it is not the end of a person's journey. These kids do not believe in reincarnation, and yet they have this unflinching conviction that they will live on in their surviving comrades, in the realization of the dream they are dying for. I sound old fashioned, even to myself, when I write this. But it is true. There is an element here that needs to be discovered, explained and transmitted to future generations.

It is bound to be a difficult task. These are a self-effacing lot. No one wants to talk about oneself. I raised this point to Wedi Ghile, as we lay side by side on the ground staring at the stars and trying to protect our nostrils and eyes from the dust being raised nearby.

"How can a *tegadalai* talk about himself?" he replied, his enormous eyes reflecting flickers from the bonfire. "He would be alienated immediately. Nothing is more despised and condemned than self-aggrandizement and boasting. But, you are right. So much heroism, so many acts of supreme sacrifice and gallantry are just passing by without being recorded. It is very sad. It has to be written." If we stay together long enough, I will ask him to narrate his experiences to me. I doubt that he will.

This struggle is just too much. Not only is it too long, it is also too hard and harsh. The trenches that I have been visiting over the past couple of days are testimony to this hardness and harshness. From where I was yesterday, I could see Volleyball to my left. For years on that hill, *tegadelti* faced the enemy's trenches only a few score meters away. Once in a while, some gallant souls would rush the distance to within reach of the other side, throw a few hand grenades at the enemy and rush back to shelter. Once in a while, the enemy would return the visit and the complement. It thus became famous for this exciting and dangerous bomb-throwing contest. So, it was nicknamed Volleyball.

There is another line of trenches called Spartacus. On most of its sides, including the one that faces the enemy, it is a chasm, a precipice that is impossible to climb or descend. They say that if you so much as miss a step or a gust of wind catches you unaware, you are in for a long jump to the bottom of the hill. The nickname is meant to indicate that, like Spartacus, *tegadalai* too has the capacity if need be, to climb down the precipice and attack enemy positions beyond.

Platoons have been known to carry the trunks of huge trees up the heights of Spartacus for building trenches. Sometimes, whenever the effort proved impossible, they would simply throw the trunk to the bottom and, no matter how high they had gone, they would climb down to fetch it back up again.

If martyrdom has become a tradition, then hard work is just life. I am with young men and women who make daily trips down all sorts of mountains and walk for hours to bring jerrycans of water all the way back to the trenches, almost without taking a rest. So far, I have not heard a single complaint from anyone. It is the commander who insists that someone take a rest. The norm is that even those who have just climbed up with a jerrycan of water volunteer for the next errand wherever it may lead. As I write, I am asking myself if this is what the revolution has created. Or is it something cultural, something inherited from the family? If independence comes, will it be preserved by the next generation and passed on to future ones?

When I was at Sulfur, I met a woman fighter, a *tegadalit* called Lemlem. Very thin and of light complexion, her hair is straight and reddish in color. She looked a bit sickly to me—like some of the women nicknamed "gastrite". Gastro-intestinal problems in women fighters is the object of a lot of light-hearted comment from everyone. A theory that all women with that ailment get cured once they married has attained strong currency within the Front. I don't know who developed that theory.

Anyway, Lemlem just sprang up from nowhere, carrying a jerrycan of water, and almost tripped over my stretched legs, as I was leaning on a rock, next to a guard-post. Someone relieved her of her load. She did not even pause to wipe sweat off her face and, showing no signs of fatigue, she said, "Hey, soul-mates, I ate *beles* and protein." *Beles* is the Tigrinya word for prickly pears. All the members of her unit dropped whatever they were doing and flocked around her, as if she were a rare specimen. "Where? Who gave you all that? I should have gone..." It was a piece of big news. The excitement was such that I could not help feeling sad. *Tegadalai* is so easy to please. Here is a breed for whom little things really mean a lot. Prickly pear and protein? The fruits yes, because they are relatively rare in Sahel. But protein? That D.M.K.-like flour that one wets or softens with simple water and struggles to swallow? In Arag it is the food to avoid, but here it is a treat.

The alternative, of course, is not anything to crave for. The regular menu here is *kitcha*, which is a flat and round bread, prepared on a large and round frying pan. The pan itself is usually the lid of a steel barrel, modified for the purpose. The "kitchen" is an amazing place to visit. Situated at least half an hour's walk from the trenches, it is a beehive of activity. Units are withdrawn from each company on a given flank and these become the cooks and bakers until they are replaced on a monthly or fortnightly basis. Barrels, sliced in half, is where the dough is prepared—sturdy men and women mixing quintals of flour and water with their bare feet. The dough is then baked on a row of ovens, which consist of the pan sitting on stone stands with fire heating it from beneath.

The sheer bulk of the bread to be thus baked make cleanliness and quality impossible. Sometimes the flour itself comes denatured or contaminated from problems of storage or from all sorts of exposure. What is more, the bread assigned to a platoon or company is usually piled on several bed sheets. These are then knotted separately to be carried away by groups assigned for the purpose. By the time these arrive at the trenches on the backs and heads of humans they have crumbled out of their original shape. Quite often, the *tomween*, which is what the general store of the brigade is known as, runs out of lentils or even salt. So units have to just settle for dry bread and some water. Small wonder then that my comrades at Sulfur envied Lemlem's treat of that morning.

The way the human body adapts itself to deprivation is something to marvel at. Compared to this, life in the base areas is one of plenty and luxury. Frankly, sometimes I am feeling very hungry. I have decided to remove even the thought of a cup of tea from the horizon of my thinking. I crave for just a sniff of cigarette smoke to satisfy my urge. I have not been here a week, but my trousers are already too large for my shrinking tummy.

No, this is a tough life. To complain about being tired, hungry or thirsty is taboo. Perseverance, suppressing one's internal feelings and desires, resisting all personal problems—even illness—is the prevailing morality and the right way to behave.

Although the same standards of behavior and morality also rule the base areas, the degree and intensity differ dramatically. Ours is more relaxed, less stringent. There is also less of the collective and more traces of the individual in the base areas. Here, everything is shared and, to that extent, frontline fighters are different. They are, for example, more hospitable and respectful than we are. Above all, it is their sense of humor that I find most fascinating and attractive. Their proximity to death probably induces in them a much lighter attitude towards life. That day on Sulfur, some of them were narrating to me the pranks and tricks that they play on one another.

The innocence and inexperience of the very young is taken advantage of by those just slightly older. They told one of them, Mebrahtu Manjus, for example, that it was possible to produce yogurt from the milk of humans. If he got the chance to go to Nakfa, they said to him, he should make sure to visit one of the *tegadelti* mothers, who would surely treat him to some of her own yogurt. The poor kid had never heard of this, but since he believed even the impossible was possible in the revolution, he believed them. He was so tempted that he even asked to go to Nakfa on an errand. When he found out that he had been fooled, he spent the day angry and secluded. Another *manjus* spent hours tantalized by the unique prospect of eating *kitcha* baked from ground seeds of prickly pears...

"We had a comrade who just could not resist hunger," Lemlem told me, remembering one of her fallen friends. "Food was so bad that he was going crazy for something nicer to eat. So, one evening he found some excuse to come to our shelter alone and stole a can of margarine from the bag of the company foot doctor. Guess what he did? He ate it or drank it, whatever, without any *kitcha*. The next morning, he told the doctor that he was suffering from dysentery and showed him his, you know...The doctor was scared by what he saw and sent him to the brigade clinic, accompanied by two comrades."

"Then what happened?"

"Well, they gave him some pills, but he was his own best doctor. He just pretended to be taking the pills. He actually preserved them in his own bag, so he would not be accused of having wasted medicine, but ate everything that came his way. He called it his honeymoon. By the time he was discharged, our food had improved. But, he did confess to the platoon leader."

"And he was not punished?"

"Why would he be punished? He was a lion in battle. He just did not know how to go hungry for one day. He was admonished at a meeting. He was so funny. He was martyred not long afterwards, he went during the Sixth Offensive." She concluded sadly.

As she was narrating the story, she and her comrades were laughing from the bottom of their hearts. I am sure that they have repeated this story over and over again and laughed as heartily upon every repetition.

Humor and laughter appear to be part of their everyday existence. They find solace in humor and laughter is how they maintain their sanity. I don't think I have ever seen a group of people who laugh, joke and dance as much as the ones I am with. What I find remarkable is that the jokes are generally upon oneself, not directed at others and, when they are, always without malice. Just as remarkable is how jokes and taunts are accepted in good humor. So far, I have not seen anyone get upset.

"Do you ever fight?" I asked Lemlem.

She gave me a suspicious and slightly condescending look. "What fights?" she asked back, "How can you talk about fighting when you know we have regular sessions of criticism and self-criticism? You are not expecting comrades bound by the same objective and principles to fight each other, are you?" She added a few more words straight from some lessons on political education. I dropped the whole topic. Fighting, too, is taboo.

The types of pastime I have been observing in the past few days include dueling against each other with sticks, pulling one another's hair, wrestling and boxing, *akhudir*—best translated as "the donkey kick"—everything accompanied by a lot of noise and laughter. I keep fearing that someone might land a stick on my behind, just to test my capacity to withstand pain.

After my chat with Lemlem and her friends at Sulfur, I talked to Wedi Ghile, the company commissioner.

"How many more days do you want to keep me here? Why don't you send me to one of the units?"

"We have been instructed to keep you with us for some time," he replied.

"But I want to be with them, to acquaint myself with their day to day life. Are you afraid I may be too old to keep pace with them?"

"Oh no, it's not that," he said shaking me by the shoulder. "You are O.K. And then, what is there that you need to get acquainted with? It is the same as the life you live at Arag. Just relax here, we will let you know when the time comes." He left me for some other business.

I could have insisted on being assigned to the trenches but I did not want to sound overly eager. However, I noted the parallel he drew between life at Arag and life in the trenches. There is, actually, no parallel. That morning at Sulfur, he was the one who had led the company into the abandoned trenches of the enemy. He was talking to me today only because the land mine he had stepped on was defective and failed to blow him up. Another member of the team had not been so lucky. He was cut to pieces and buried right on the spot. This is what Wedi Ghile described as "the same life" with that in Arag. Well, hardly.

## 6 August 1985

We left Kertset late last night and we are in Nakfa today. Assahaita is the commander of the first company, ours is the third. Assahaita is his nickname. It means very cold, biting wind. The nickname implies that his fighting ways send a chill down the enemy's spine.

He has a long, lean and strikingly handsome face. His eyes are sharp but sad at the same time. His physique is proportionate and well structured. He was lying under the shade of a tree when I joined him earlier this morning. We sat for a while without talking, watching the whole battalion moving around to settle for the day. Some had already gone to the outskirts of Nakfa and were coming back with loads of prickly pears on their shoulders.

Suddenly, he started talking in a sing-song voice. "Is the Front in its right senses? Why has it suddenly decided to send all you educated and professional people here? Weren't you where you should be?"

I did not know how to reply to that. I mumbled something in response, something indicating approval of the decision.

"Come on," he said, interrupting my incoherence, "I am not happy, not happy at all. Look, everyone is here. Engineer, teacher...are we all going to perish together? This is simply not good."

I did not say anything, and he did not continue with the topic. After a while, he called someone from one of his platoons and said, "Why are you being so unfair to us? How can you eat all that *beles* by yourselves? Couldn't you, at least, be generous to my guest here? How about Assahaita the Poor, has he ever said that he does not like *beles*?"

The young *tegadalai* laughed, obviously enjoying Assahaita's feigned feelings of hurt. "We are cooling juicy ones for you in a large container of water," he said, running to another shade. In a few minutes, we were enjoying the coolness of the fruits. I am not much of a *beles* eater, but I ate until I belched its taste a couple of times. Assahaita must have eaten double mine. *Beles* is nice to eat, but it creates a problem on its way out!

We were lying side by side, staring at the slightly moving leaves above us, when Assahaita said, "Describe the base area to me. They tell me Arareb is like a city."

I looked at him in surprise, "Have you never been there?"

"How can I ever be there? Look at our life. It is always from one trench to the other, one battle to the next. When there are lulls in fighting, it is always digging new trenches or repairing old ones. Add the intensive academic lessons and political education and what do you have? No leisure time at all. You can't go to the base areas unless you are wounded and the damned bullet just keeps avoiding me."

"You pray for a bullet just to see Arareb?"

He smiled mischievously, "You know, the one that just grazes you on the flesh but hurts enough to send you to Arareb and back? That's what I mean. I couldn't stand permanent disability. But tell me about those places."

I tried to describe Arareb for him. The underground boarding school that hosts about four thousand students; Orota Hospital, which visitors have nicknamed "the longest hospital in the world"; the pharmaceutical factory, the metal and wood workshops...etc. Some of these, I had not even seen myself, so I included in my list what I had merely heard about. His appetite for knowledge seemed insatiable. His questions extended into current international affairs, the latest inventions and even the workings of satellites.

"*Mbwa,* some of your questions are too tough for me. I don't know the answer to many of them."

"You carry this big head on your shoulders and with all your hair and beard, you can't answer my questions? I am gong to milk all that knowledge out of you while you are with us. How else can Assahaita the Poor gain any education? What does he know apart from shooting guns?"

"You are saying this for the second time. Why do you keep calling yourself Assahaita the Poor?"

"But I am poor," he answered good-naturedly. "When I came here, I brought only one thing along with me, my soul. When the time comes, I'll take it with me. Do you have a better definition of poverty?"

"You may be poor in the material sense," I insisted, partly to provoke him, "but you do not seem to suffer from any spiritual poverty."

"Hey, hey, don't ever let spiritual poverty near you. That will mean degeneration. That will mean being despised and discarded like those decayed *beles* we have refused to eat. The wealth of *tegadalai* is his perseverance and his spiritual purity. We lose that, we are no more. But, in other ways, we are poor my friend...and Assahaita is the poorest of them all."

He was sitting up when he said this. He then lifted his head towards the sky and started to sing to some tune I could not recognize. His words were clear, "Poor, oh, you poor Assahaita...." He repeated the phrase several times.

I laughed deeply and sincerely and liked him very much. I would have loved to hear him talk some more, but one of the platoon leaders called him over and he left me where I was. I wrote this immediately after he left.

*7 August 1985*

We spent the night at Embalko, the same place we had stayed the first night. It is about 45 minutes walk northwest of Nakfa. All the companies of our battalion have assembled together. Today, I spent a lot of time with people I knew from before. One of them was Chu Chu.

Her actual name is Semainesh Ghebreweldi, but we call her Chu Chu. In 1976, she came to Sahel to study at the Revolution School. Her parents stayed behind in the refugee camps of Sudan. She was about twelve years old at the time. She may be twenty-one now. She is short and stockily built. She has very short and dark hair and a light round face to match it. I noticed that she has still retained the charming smile of her childhood. She was one of my favorite pupils when I taught at the school in the late seventies and very early eighties.

As the years passed, she developed quite a tough attitude towards life and the rough environment she was growing up in. She was stubborn about whatever she believed to be the truth, and she was always at the forefront, even in the most tasking physical work.

One day, an adolescent who had been bullying all the boys and girls in the school tried to harass her. Without hesitating, she challenged him to a wrestle and knocked him down in front of a number of onlookers. The whole school heard about this and, from then onwards, she walked tall amongst her peers.

I mentioned this to her when she came to see me this afternoon. She smiled. We talked about the Revolution School and the time they passed there. She seemed to miss even the worst aspects of life in that school. She felt particularly nostalgic and sad when she went down that list of those of her classmates who had died in the fighting.

"Are you married, yet?" I asked her, probably to change the topic.

She laughed and stared into my eyes, imitating my gestures. She quickly turned serious and said, "Don't talk to me about marriage. My attention is not there."

"Why not?"

"Do you know who I am left with here? Look at them," she said, pointing to the *tegadelti* who were jumping and kicking all over the place. "Almost everyone here came after the Sixth Offensive in '82. Many joined us after Selahta in '83. Everyone has gone and I hate every minute that I live after them. You talk about marriage."

"You want every one to die, right? I find it ridiculous whenever you people say that."

She smiled pensively and said, "Surviving your peers, your fellow students and your friends is the worst that can happen to you." She fell silent for a while and then changed the subject, "Are they serious about mobilizing you to the frontlines?"

"Of course."

"Why don't they let you be in the base areas? Why don't you just stay there and lay the foundation for the future?" She was also teasing me.

"But you need some respite here. In fact, I have come to take your place for a few weeks," I teased back, tapping her shoulder.

"Now? At your age?" She said ruffling my hair and shaking her head, "You are all gray already, it's incredible. I wish you had not come here."

"Why not?"

"Because you have come to bury your children."

It was as if she had pierced my heart with a spear. I sprang at her in quick response and grabbed her by the hand.

"What kind of talk was that?" I said angrily, but she easily freed herself from my grip and ran a few meters in playful panic.

"If we don't leave early in the morning, I'll come and see you. I'll bring a bar of soap along to wash your hair and remove your lice." She left.

The sun is setting. It is getting too dark for me to write more. I feel as if a heavy load is just sitting on my chest. I am almost choking and her words keep ringing in my ears. She did not utter those words out of spite or any malice. But, for her to take her own death for granted and my survival as guaranteed is just too much to swallow. I feel as if she is accusing me while still alive. No wonder she feels guilty for having survived her own peers and friends. Maybe she feels that she has lost her right to stay alive. She is blaming herself for having been outpaced in the rush towards the ultimate sacrifice. If they tell me she is dead tomorrow, I will probably feel the same way and say the same thing.

Naughty, Chu Chu. She is making me blabber in raw philosophy.

Such a combination of heart-rending little incidents and encounters makes death something to yearn for.

### 9 August 1985

We are still at Embaleko. Chu Chu has gone without washing my hair or relieving me of these pestering lice.

I spent the day with Gobbo, which is the Italian word for bent. He stoops when he walks. It is just nicknames everywhere. Gobbo was one of the senior administrators at the EPLF Department of the Economy. He is now a platoon commander. I was surprised to see him in shorts, with two bombs and a neatly folded bed sheet firmly strapped to his waist, moving up and down with impressive agility.

"How do you manage? What is the secret?" I asked him.

"Acceptance," he answered in a matter-of-fact tone. "Never over-estimate the life of the soldier. Start from scratch and learn everything step by step. Never give up. In battle, control yourself, never get excited; study the enemy's intention and try to guess the direction of the bullet. Above all, learn from comrades, you'll be there."

### 11 August 1985

We left Embaleko the day before yesterday. With Nakfa to the south west, the whole battalion passed through Wegret, climbed a steep slope and descended an escarpment to arrive at Emkma. Clouds and a breeze cooled the heat from the sun and the march. This area is also relatively cooler. The mountains and hills are covered by such trees and vegetation that include sisal, cactus and some olive trees. The scenery itself dissipated some of our fatigue.

Along the way, I tried to keep pace with Wedi Ghil'u, one of the leaders of the battalion who had lost an eye in some previous battle. He speaks Tigre and Tigrinya with equal ease and fluency. He must have lived in these areas, for he seems to know every turn and every stone.

Emkema is located at the bottom of an escarpment, about a ninety-minute walk from Wegret. Now, it has been turned into a refugee camp. "Emkema" means, "the mother of a constellation," Wedi Ghil'u told us. Just as the stars in a constellation seem to flock to or proceed towards a center, so do the mountains, hills and vegetation of this whole environment seem to rush towards Emkema.

Its name is well deserved. It is a spot of green lawns and big trees whose names I simply do not know. Their leaves are so closely knit in some places that they come close to forming a forest. A stream runs through the greenery and the water is sweet, not salty as is the case in Nakfa and elsewhere in this area. It is, in short, an attractive place, quite a break from the dreary barrenness of the hills and ravines that one gets accustomed to in Sahel.

We saw many refugees at Emkema, mostly women and children. I also saw small gardens by the stream where the refugees grow tomatoes and hot pepper. I felt a pang of joy at getting a glimpse of the attempt by the refugees to live normal lives in the midst of war and destruction.

Emkema is located at the foot of the Rora Mountains. These are an elevated range that proudly command the Nakfa landscape for kilometers on end. For centuries, their ragged boulders, thick forests and fierce leopards had made them formidable to the visits or conquest of outsiders. Only their inhabitants enjoyed the security and comfort they offered.

In 1983, during the Dergue's "Stealth" Offensive, Ethiopian troops dared to scale their heights for the first time in this twenty-four year-old war of liberation. It was a bold and dangerous move on the part of the Ethiopians, as they would have positioned themselves behind the EPLF's trenches at Nakfa. But the Roras were not occupied for long. The EPLF launched a major drive against the intruders and the Roras regained their old status.

Not quite, though. Previously, only man and animals could scale their heights. Today, army trucks and four-wheel pickups crisscross them at will. During the battle for their control, the Ethiopians and the EPLF had built roads up their southern and eastern slopes, respectively. That has taken some of their mystery and quite a bit of their natural majesty away from them.

The EPLF's road starts up just a few hundred meters to the north of Emkema. It twists and bends up the frightening elevation like a creeping giant snake. It is a feat of skill and hard work that EPLF engineers and builders should be proud of. Just a few TNT explosives, lots of picks, hoes and spades...the rest is ingenuity, hard work and, of course, an "it can be done" attitude.

We had started from Nakfa at 5 A.M. We arrived at Hashfet at 11:00 or about noon. We had been climbing and descending so much that I could not figure out where exactly Hashfet was located. I still can't. All I know now is that we walked for two hours to get to it from Emkema. Hashfet is so totally surrounded by mountains that it has the shape of a bowl. It is, actually, dried riverbed whose outlet is a chasm of boulders that drops twenty to thirty meters on its southern side.

I was exhausted. I was also sweating so profusely that my shirt was pasted to my back. I was making an effort not to look the way I felt, but my face and general condition was obviously betraying me. As I sat on a flat rock next to where Assahaita was already resting, sweat had totally drenched my beard. It had also dried around my temples and parts of my cheeks. I must have been quite a spectacle— probably, pale and salty. Assahaita took one look at me and started laughing. "Barba," he said, referring to my beard, "how are you finding the Forces?" The EPLF's fighting units were always referred to as "Forces."

I did not give him a direct reply. I just examined his face closely. Except for what looked like sprinkles of water on his forehead, there was no sign of sweat on any part of him. "Do you sweat?" I asked him.

"I don't know, maybe I do. I guess there are two types of sweating. Some, like yourself, sweat outwards. Others, like myself, sweat inwards." I laughed and felt better enough to examine, with my eyes, the roughness of the terrain around Hashfet.

"Take good note of all these mountains. Maybe someday you will write about them," Assahaita said to me. "During the Selahta Offensive, Hashfet was the Headquarter of the Nakfa Front. It was the hub of our whole strategy of defense. All the logistics for this front, food and ammunition, had to be transported to the trenches on the backs of *tegadelti*. It took us five hours to get here from Nakfa, right? *Tegadelti* had to carry their wounded comrades on stretchers, all the way to Nakfa."

A platoon commander sitting across from us shook his head to emphasize Assahaita's memories. "Don't talk about Selahta," he said. "I don't think we will ever face an experience as difficult and horrible as that one. The challenge we faced here, the insurmountable difficulties we had to overcome...." He sighed and fell silent.

We stayed at Hashfet until 4 P.M. yesterday. Everyone slept, but I could not. Anything keeps me awake—a mosquito whining above me, a fly landing on my face or lice creeping, tickling and biting me all over. Assahaita and the rest just slept, as if mosquitoes, flies and lice were not treating all of us the same.

At four, we left Hashfet and proceeded due southwest, always with the Rora Mountains to our right. We passed Bet Humed and a large seasonal river that joins the river Hiday, which itself flows between the towns of Nakfa and Afabet. From this point on, the trenches came in full view of our higher and more commanding positions. Some of the trenches, for example at Swara and Afintcha, have been alternating between the enemy and our side. Someone was telling me about this. But the number of battles fought on this front are so many that I have simply given up attempting to keep a decent record.

We walked for two hours from Hashfet to the trenches that were to be our resting place for the night. All the way to our left, and from a safe distance, I could see the opposing trenches of the EPLF and the enemy. It seems that there is nothing in this whole area except trenches. The only humans I have seen are my own comrades, fully armed. Nothing happens here except war. I remember someone telling me once that he believed God had created Sahel so that we may one day draw our enemy to it and defeat him in its rough and thirsty terrain. I am not much of a believer but maybe he was right.

As I write this, I am sitting in full view of a huge mountain range called, the Sigad. In one part, it takes the shape of the hump of a bullock, and its western edge spreads to the foot of the Laba, which is a prominent part of the Rora. On the western flank of Sigad are three ridges where Ethiopian brigades have entrenched themselves. The top of the range is well-fortified, with what looks like the Great Wall of China straddling its length. In some parts, two more "Great Walls" have been built below the top or the ridge. Thus, Sigad has, not just one but three lines of defense on the same slope. I am now wondering how such heavy fortifications are dislodged....

This is my ninth day with the Forces. In my opinion, and taking my age and experience into consideration, the number of mountains I have climbed through these nine days is unparalleled. I have also developed a very ingenious technique of scaling mountains. There is nothing easier and more effective than observing and following the footsteps of those striding and ascending in front of you. The day before yesterday, Assahaita and Bahre Debbas were alternating, leading the rest of us up a stiff climb. Assahaita's footwork was easier to follow and imitate, while Bahre's steps came in such quick and awkward sequences that, at one point, I fell face forward and almost lost my front teeth.

"Are you alright?" they shouted, not even bothering to look back or wait for my reply. I had to make an effort to pick myself up and run the distance to stay close enough to those steps, strides, shuffles and stumbles that have now become my only inspiration. They march and I follow, refusing to look up at the disheartening heights yet to be climbed. Once on top of a hill, I look down and pride myself at the feats already accomplished….

### 13 August 1985

It is 5 P.M. Last night we climbed up Rora Laba, which is one of the prominent plateaus on top of the Rora Mountains. Yesterday, after a long and back-breaking travel, we spent the greater part of the day on a hill known as Desiet, which means island. In a terrain that is full of ranges of mountains, it stands alone and aloof just like an island.

I tried to take a nap under a nice shade right on the top. As I was drowsing into deep sleep, something soft touched my lips and nose, as if caressing me. I opened my eyes and saw a huge rat climbing up my face. I started up and it ran into some hole. I hate rats, but I tried to ignore it in the hope that it would not come back. I was soon asleep, but I felt its heavy weight once again running up and down my whole body.

I don't think I ever saw a rat that big—maybe in my childhood, at the toilets and sewers of the Hospital Regina Elena in Asmara from where they used to scare children. I sat up and tried to scare this one off, but it kept returning. I had a stick. When it came near, I landed a heavy blow on its back. It did not even look hurt. It simply jumped up into the air, paused for a moment and looked ready to run away. I hit it again, harder this time. It wouldn't die, but it was too hurt to run. So, it tried to crawl to its hideout. I was not enjoying what I was doing, but I landed two more blows on its back and it died.

With a great deal of disgust and probably also a little shame at having overcome the little creature, I picked it by the tail and threw it as far away from me as I could. But I could not go back to sleep. I guess it was its size and its refusal to succumb to my blows that haunted me most. Seven or eight of its type could probably eat a grown man.

At two o'clock we left Desiet and traveled due west towards Hohot, which is the gate to the plateaus of Rora Laba. The escarpment we took opens up such an exciting scenery that, this time, the whole ascent was like a pleasure trip. We passed through vegetation rich in aloe plants, and olive trees, with dots of ebony gracing the landscape.

At Hohot, the topography changes dramatically. Rora Laba is a plateau that is broken by hills, slopes and falls. What flat area is available here is used for intensive farming. So, it looks a lot like the *Kebessa,* although I am yet to see a settled village. All I have seen so far are isolated *hdmos* built exactly in *Kebessa* style.

A long time ago, the ancestors of the people who presently live in the Rora migrated here from Adi Nefas, a village about five kilometers north of Asmara. They were settled agriculturalists who spoke Tigrinya and practiced the Christian religion. To the Roras, they brought their farming skills, land tenure system and a settled, as opposed to nomadic, agrarian lifestyle. But mixing with the previous settlers of the Roras, they eventually dropped their language and religion to adopt the Tigre tongue and the Moslem faith. In the process, they also introduced a highly structuralized, feudal system of administration of which they became the rulers. So, the plateaus of the Rora and Nakfa are a place where Eritrean cultures, faiths, lifestyles and history blend in a very interesting mix.

No wonder then that this looks so much like *Kebessa*. As I write this, I feel as if I am in the vicinity of Afdeo or Tzehaflam. a few kilometers north of Asmara. It has been eleven years since I left those areas, so this whole surrounding brings nostalgic memories of my own carefree childhood. But, sadly, there are no trees within sight of me. Amongst the hills and plains that span my vision, I see a few olive trees that have either dried up or are about to. No young olives and, worse, no other trees. Oral history blames the Italians for having mercilessly deforested this once rich flora.

I am sitting on one of the trenches that the enemy had used only two years ago, during the Selahta Offensive. In my vicinity, are old shoes thrown away by the Dergue's soldiers, rusted tin cans from which they ate or drank and the remains of their skeletons—an arm here, a jaw with some missing teeth there...

It is not a good sight. As I look as far as my eyes can see, I would be hard pressed to say that we are experiencing a drought again this year. Compared to the rocky dryness of the rest of Sahel, where I have spent my last eleven years, this looks green and lush. But the scanty rain that has fallen this season has only enabled some grass to grow and a few Meskel flowers to bloom. Crops have failed. Worse still, this whole area comes under constant enemy bombardment from the positions I described earlier. Ordinary people cannot live here in safety. Throughout yesterday and today, I have seen only some cattle and sheep herded by very few young boys. No men or women around.

In place of people and crops, it is just rusted tins, discarded boots, ammunition shells and shrapnel of all description, bombs and rockets that failed to explode and, yes, the exposed bones of human beings. Far away, are the trenches of the enemy looking up at our own commanding positions. War and all its hateful symbols command in Laba...the Laba of 1985. No, not just Laba, this is the picture of Eritrea in the eighties.

### 20 August, 1985
I have not written this past week. Today, I write with a heavy and disturbed heart. Let me start a bit earlier.

On August 17, I was assigned to one of our three platoons as a political commissioner. My company commander, Bahre Debbas, told me about this.

"But I know nothing about the administration of fighting units," I protested. "I want to join the rank and file."

"Stop arguing, my friend. You can administer much more. When you are told to go around here, you just go." He put me in my place.

After my brief experience in 1975, I have not seen direct battle-field action. "One has to have a good idea, at least, of the direction of the sound of gunshot before leading a platoon," I grumbled while collecting my meager belongings. I left without a word.

So, I am with the platoon today. The platoon leader's name is Ghebremeskel Berhe, better known as Wedi Berhe. He cannot control his right foot, it just drops with a flat sound as he walks. He is what they call, "a nerve injury." The commissioner I am replacing is nicknamed, "Gordem." He denies this vehemently, but he apparently mispronounced Gordon Scott's first name in a casual conversation. No one calls him anything else but "Gordem." He too has a damaged right foot. Both of these colleagues took turns to introduce me to the life, culture and administration of the "Force."

But, let me go back to the source of my present disquiet. After having distanced myself from the rest of the platoon for three days, I decided to end my self-imposed isolation by joining some of them in a game of volleyball. That was yesterday afternoon. As I approached them, they all gave me a suspicious look and continued with their warm up.

Among the group was a former student of mine called Melake from my days at the Revolution School. Perhaps to break the tension or out of respect for me, he suggested that a young man named Wedi Ghirmai and myself become captains and choose our respective teams from those assembled.

"Why don't you become the captain? You and Wedi Ghirmai select teams from the rest of us," I replied as amiably as I could. Melake refused and we wrestled playfully, just like the old days at the school.

I heard the others laugh. When Melake and myself rejoined them hand in hand, I could see that all the tension had evaporated. I regretted not having done that much earlier. It cost me three days of loneliness.

We played two games of volleyball. The ball, of course, was made of rags and two poles with a rope connecting them served as the net. The field is the flattest spot on the slope behind our present trenches. Our game attracted the rest of the platoon and it developed into a highly contested match.

Some meters from where we were playing I could see Kidan, from Adi Shuma, in the vicinity of Massawa. He was reading to the prettiest girl in the whole company. Earlier that morning, he had come to the "office" of the platoon looking for the third grade book on General Science. He was probably explaining something to her. The way they sat, pressing against each other, made me suspect that they might be lovers. I stole two or three glances of envy at them.

The game ended about 6 P.M. Wedi Berhe and Gordem had not been with us throughout the day. They came immediately after the game and we ate dinner. At about 7:00 P.M. Wedi Berhe called me aside and told me that he was going to send a reconnaissance unit behind enemy lines.

"Is it safe to do so? How far are they going?" I asked.

"It's nothing," he replied. "Our company has never been to these areas. We need to study it. They will be back within two hours." For him, it was just a normal, day to day affair.

It was already dark when we went to see them off. Five of them were standing at the edge of a steep slope, waiting for instructions. I was feeling a little uneasy about the whole thing and I wanted to know who exactly we were sending on this errand. So, I approached them to get a closer look.

One was Ghebru Agefa, a unit leader who, for the previous three nights, had been sharing a mat with me next to the guard post. We had been alternating in keeping time for exchanging night guards. The second man was Kidan, the one who looked so romantic a couple of hours earlier, reading to that pretty girl. Third was Melake, my former young student. The fourth man, Berhane, had earlier been pointed out to me as being fierce and courageous in the battle field. The fifth person I could not recognize.

It was so dark and windy that Wedi Berhe's instructions seemed to come from somewhere far away. Even now, more that twenty hours later, some of his words still ring in my ears. "Stick to the right of this pass," he was saying. "If you stray to your left as you go or to your right as you return, you will step on landmines. Take extreme caution...."

I did not hear him out. My mind had already drifted away. Years in the Revolution School and in cultural work have, I guess, developed within me an interest in men and women as individuals—in their internal feelings and personal fate, in the details of their character and in their private hidden desires. These are normally suppressed by the collective spirit that pervades the whole organization. So, I stopped listening to Wedi Berhe and got even closer to each member of the team in an attempt to read as much from their faces as the dim light of the flickering stars allowed. I also helped Melake fold his *netsela*.

All five of them were not uttering a word. They just stood calm and composed, listening to the directives of their leader. I could see no outward manifestation of whatever internal fears or doubts they might have had. No one is more aware than the *tegadalai*, of the imminence and suddenness of his own death. Yet, his acceptance or defiance of this finality, of this cruel termination to life whose mere possibility terrifies all human beings, transcends all limits. Above all else, this realization dominated my whole thinking yesterday evening.

At about 7 P.M. we watched them climb down the pass and disappear into the darkness. Gordem offered to help me keep time for our night guards. As we stumbled up to the guard-post, I found it difficult to contain my internal misgivings.

"What do we do if something unexpected happens to them? Send re-enforcements?" I asked Gordem.

"Well, if they fall into an enemy trap, they'll have to find their own way out. If they can, they should make their escape without firing a shot. But, if they step on a land mine, we'll have to run for them with our stretchers."

Gordem and I lay side by side, a few meters from the guard-post and talked for quite a while. I was keeping time and, by 9 P.M. I assigned the first guard. We must have dozed off. About half an hour later, the sound of a loud explosion startled both of us to a sitting position. Gordem asked me to stay with the guards and rushed down the trenches. There was no doubt that a land mine had exploded. I closed my eyes and the composed faces of our five gallant men appeared before me.

"Which one?" I asked myself over and over again. I am not experienced in this sort of thing and I certainly do not have a military attitude. So, frankly, I started to feel quite uneasy and very guilty for having been amongst those who had ordered the errand. Once or twice, I tried to admonish myself for being too soft and for failing to expect such inevitabilities. But I was too agitated to listen even to my own voice....

Gordem came back at about midnight. The wind was whistling and Laba was very, very cold. He found me waiting in restless anticipation.

"A land mine almost finished them off," he said, not waiting for my question. "They accomplished their mission without a hitch, but Ghebru Agefa strayed on their way back and stepped on one."

"So?"

"He's been hit on both legs. The rest are all safe. We were lucky tonight." He spread his *netela* and covered his face.

There was no change in his tone of voice, but I suspected something more must have happened. So, I took Ghebru Agefa for dead. Considering what could have happened, I thought even that was lucky and almost consoled myself. I spent a disturbed night, trying to put in some sleep between each exchanging guard.

At 6 A.M. this morning, I was climbing down from the trenches and heading for our shelter when Gordem pulled me aside. "I didn't want you to spend a sleepless night," he said. "That explosive did not spare us."

"My heart skipped a beat" is an expression I had only heard about. It did this morning.

"Melake, Kidan and Berhane didn't make it. They died on the spot. Agefa has been hit. Only one has come back intact...."

I just could not believe what I was hearing. Consternation cannot explain my state of mind of this morning. It went beyond that. I am writing this at 5 P.M. Even now, pangs of shock keep jolting me back to the incident. Yesterday, at exactly this time, I was playing volleyball with Melake, I threw a couple of envious glances at Kidan and his partner and I could see Berhane wrestle from a distance...and now? Try as I may, I can neither comprehend nor accept what has happened.

As soon as Gordem told me of the tragedy, I went straight to my shade and got into a miserable mood. I just did not know how to react or behave. What do you do under such circumstances? Philosophize? Pretend as if nothing has happened and just talk and joke as usual? Or do you wrap yourself with your *netsela* and attempt to sleep it away...? I have chosen to write.

But I cannot express everything that I am feeling. I've been picking and dropping my pen for hours and feeling so inadequate as a writer that it is frustrating. One question keeps haunting me though. How long are our young men and women going to be mauled like this? It is too sad, too damned painful. Melake, little Melake's death, is literally, eating into me. I knew him better than the others, he was my student. I had not seen him in a few years. When I first did a few days ago, we hugged. He was too shy to talk to me at any length. After that, I saw him only yesterday, not 24 hours ago yet. I chased him playfully, we played volleyball and exchanged a few old jokes. He is no more. He and his comrades are buried at Abi L'ba, in some obscure and rocky nowhere, on the edges of Laba.

Maybe Chu Chu was right. Maybe I have come to "bury my children," I don't know. I wish there was another way of gaining our independence, something other than revolution, the struggle, and war. Our revolution is too costly. This struggle is too bitter.

Wedi Berhe came back late this morning. He must have been burying them the whole night. His eyes were blood-shot. I could easily see that he was burning inside, but he gave a brave exterior. He smiled at me and said, "We lost such a choice of men for nothing. You know, these are the type who capture enemy garrisons." He shook his head and went straight to his administrative chores. He allotted some new clothing to those in need. He then gave one long look at the bloodstained rubber sandals of the dead comrades, called three from the platoon whose sandals were a load of patches, and told them to wash and wear the dead men's shoes. Exhausted, he lay by my side to take a well-deserved nap. He must have started dreaming immediately or maybe he was reliving the horrors of the night. He jerked a couple of times before going into deep sleep.

A few minutes ago, my company commander, Bahre Debbas, interrupted my writing to chat with me for a while. We exchanged a few words and then he said, "Did you see how those kids perished last night?"

I mumbled something in reply. He shook his head. "They were dumb," he continued. "How could they miss a path they had already gone through? Not only that, they were also huddling together, they should have come in single file and quite apart from each other."

I did not want him to talk about them in that tone and manner, so I said, "Maybe the darkness confused them."

"Well, and this is the result! Military mistakes are corrected by death. They are not like political mistakes where you say you accept criticism, promise never to repeat the same error in the future... and nonsense like that. You make a mistake here, you're finished. A soldier must avoid errors."

Bahre has only one eye. I looked at it intently. His tough words not withstanding, his one remaining eye could not hide the sorrow and tension inside him.

But I just learned something from him. A *tegadalai* is also a soldier. He has no time for sorrow, sentimentality and sympathy. He should learn to accept things as they come. He examines, prioritizes, weighs or assesses them in relation to their military benefits or costs and to their soldierly rationality or irrationality. Then, if there is time for sympathy and sentimentality, if....


### Ten Years Later

*September 1995*
A few weeks ago, friends encouraged me to collect some of my writings from the field and prepare them for publishing. While leafing through my old notebooks, I came across the accounts I kept from the 3rd to the 20th of August 1985. These were what I have recounted above.

I do not remember why I stopped recording my observations after the 20th of August. Maybe I was too overwhelmed by the happenings of the week that followed. My mind still teems with many of the details of those few eventful days. Reconstructing them now, ten years later, will be difficult. I regret that I failed to capture the emotions of the moment in my diary.

On August 21, 1985, the day after I wrote about Melake and his comrades, we were ordered to leave Laba and go back to Nakfa. We reached Hashfet late in the afternoon and found Mercedes trucks waiting to take us. As we boarded them, it started to rain heavily. Wedi Berhe and myself were in the cabin with the driver. We were already wet as we got inside. The rest of the platoon was soaking at the back of the truck.

Wedi Berhe had a very sudden way of saying things and this endeared him to his comrades. He is still alive.

"I was hoping you would help me with my academic studies," he said to me.

"I can still do that. We are still together," I answered.

"Well, I don't know. There's some action awaiting us tonight. We'll have a very hectic few days."

His right leg was so badly damaged that I kept wondering why he carried on with the Forces. Like many others, he probably refused to part from them. A lot of fighters did not know how to live anywhere else.

It was about eight in the evening when we arrived at Nakfa. We found the town bustling with activity. Some were twisting their *net-sela* into a knot. Others were counting jerrycans or cleaning and checking their guns. They were waiting for us. We had "protein" for dinner and were treated to gallons full of "third world milk," which must be the lowest quality of powdered milk that comes in paper sacks. I had such a fill that my belly ached.

Soon we were called to a meeting. The battalion commander, Haileab Manjus, spoke first. I don't remember what he said, but I recall admiring his oratory. Next spoke Assahaita. "We need to act fast," he was saying. "If we employ speed and the usual military caution in the first few minutes, we will not encounter any problem."

We were told to relax until we were assigned to our battle positions. Our battalion was to launch the first attack on the next morning. Previously, I had only heard fighters talk about the jitters on the eve of battle. I experienced them that night. Using my jacket as a pillow, I remember attempting to sleep on the ground covered by stone and pebbles. I could not. One thought dominated my whole mind.

"What will tomorrow this time look like?" I kept asking myself.

"Who will survive and who will not?" I would be dishonest if I were to deny that my chief worry was whether I, myself, would live to see the stars of the following evening.

Next to me, my younger comrades were already in deep sleep. Apparently the stones and pebbles were not bothering them. I envied them with all my heart. Lack of sleep was to be my chief antagonist over the next four days.

About midnight, we moved towards our fighting positions. We stopped when we reached "Fidel Pe," which was how the trenches right at the top of the winding road to Afabet were known. When it looked like this was going to be a long pause, I strayed to Assahaita's company, trying to locate my colleagues from Arag. It was so dark that I had to peer into each face to find someone I recognized.

I heard a voice call my name. It was Tesfai Orologio, so named because he was a watch-repair man in one of the famous streets of Asmara.

"Who are you looking for?" he asked me.

"Oromo," I replied.

"You can't find him here. He is way forward with the advance team."

We exchanged a few words. He had joined the revolution along with his wife and five children. All the children had attended the Revolution School and so I knew them all well. As I was talking to him, they were told to move on.

He tapped me on the shoulder and said, "*Bouna fortuna*, we'll meet in victory." Later, I found out that he died in one of the first assaults early next morning.

I went back to my platoon and sat for a while. Someone came to lead us to our position, right beside the road we were resting on. I have since passed up and down that road several times, but I always fail to locate where exactly we spent the rest of that night. I just am not good at finding and following directions. Anyway, three of us shared a shelter until dawn started to break. I can still feel the silence of that stifling place. All that could be heard was the occasional sound of our shifting feet.

About 6 A.M. we heard the sound of gunfire to the east of our position. A unit leader, a well-structured woman called Letebrhan

was sitting beside me. She sprang up and peered through the small
window of the shelter that also served as the firing post.

"Our comrades are assaulting," she told us. "It is Assahaita's
company. It is light enough to see. Come take a look."

She left the post and I stuck my head into the window. The sun
was about to rise, but I could not figure out what was taking place
across the valley from us. "Can you see? Look at the treeless spot on
the right. There's a huge mound there. That's where they are attacking."

One needed trained eyes and ears in order to locate the exact
source of the sound of gunfire. Letebrhan noted my confusion and
just pulled me down from the post to reoccupy it herself. "Yes," she
kept saying after every volley of machine gun and rifle fire, "they'll
take it now." She almost killed me with anticipation.

About twenty minutes into the assault, though, she started to
fidget. "Ah, a clumsy battle, totally uncoordinated,' she said. I did
not like what she was saying, so I tried to refrain from commenting.
"They should have destroyed them by now. Those asses are holding
out!"

Half an hour passed...forty minutes...the "clumsy battle" showed
no sign of improvement. With every passing second, Letebrhan's
impatience mounted vividly. "My comrades, my beloved comrades,
this is not our day...." She left the firing post and went out of the
shelter. I replaced her at the post once again and tried to see and
understand. All I could hear was the sound of heavy rifle combat. I
still wonder how that woman of 23 could discern clumsiness from
the confusing sound that was reaching me. I felt inept.

She came rushing back. "I told you," she said. "They are holding their own. Those rotten garbage! They are taking heroes away
from us, you understand?"

She rocked the calmness of our shelter with a monologue of
angry protest at not being among those clearly suffering a setback.
Her will power, her utter contempt for fire and death stupefied me.
I was about to say something by way of consolation when a member
of our platoon peeped his head into our shelter and told us to rush
after him fully armed. The whole company emerged from shelters
and fox-holes, jumped out of the trenches, climbed down into a dry

river bed and started running towards the scene of fighting.

My forty-first birthday was approaching the following October. A few minutes into the running, I started to realize that keeping pace with my comrades, most of them hardly out of their teens, was bound to become quite an ordeal. Right in front of us was a big mountain called "Kuomintang." It was an enemy stronghold that often proved treacherous to the Eritrean side: hence "Kuomintang", to denote its anti-socialist, anti-patriotic nature. Beyond it to our right was a cone shaped hill from where a 14.5 mm gun was firing salvoes directly towards us. It made a deafening sound. We were out in the open with neither trees nor high ground to protect us. A woman nicknamed "Aunt Ho", from a fictional character in a Vietnamese short story, was hit. She fell right in front of me. One person fell back to help her. The rest of us just jumped over her and continued to run.

I do not know how far we went. When we reached a rocky area, though, I understood why Letebrhan had been so upset. Some twenty wounded comrades were huddling at the foot of a huge rock. A man called Damba, who was Assahaita's political commissar, was lying there wounded on the leg. He waved at me. I could see from their faces that the morning had been disastrous for their company.

A few meters from the rock, the riverbed broke into a narrow gorge full of stones, rocks and huge boulders. It seemed that Assahaita's company had fallen into a trap and it needed some re-enforcement to ease its problem from behind or the sides, I still don't know which. Nine people from our platoon started to descend the gorge. I joined them. The gorge opened to sprawling ground some two hundred meters further down, where part of the enemy trenches were situated. We were safe until we reached halfway down the steep slope. Suddenly, a salvo of machine gun fire forced the ten of us to veer to our left and seek protection.

The RPG (Rocket Propelled Grenade) man of the platoon was nicknamed "Sinnom", which means "toothy", obviously because he had huge front teeth. He pointed to a jutting boulder with a small cave on its side. We all crowded behind its relative safety. Apart from Sinnom, Letebrhan was also in the group, along with Lemlem, the one everyone envied at Sulfur for having eaten "protein and *beles*."

"Tish'ate", meaning "nine" , because he had only nine fingers, was the the unit leader. A young and witty youngster called Wedi Ghirmai and four others I do not remember now formed the whole group.

. It was 7 A.M. when we first hid behind the boulder. For almost six hours, we stayed there crowded together. That is one experience that still lives with me. Across the valley from us was an enemy machine gunner, who had seen us come down the gorge and knew where we were hiding. He made it a point to aim at our position and maintain an incessant volley of machine gun fire. Many of the bullets hit the jutting rock that was protecting us. At intervals shells from 81 mm mortars also fell in our vicinity.

Soon we realized that we had been completely trapped. Later I also learned that enemy soldiers had been attempting to break into our gorge and either capture or finish us off. However, what was important was not the fact that we were in some form of encirclement. I knew that *tegadelti* had often found themselves in much bigger and more dramatic entrapments, from where they had escaped in feats of courage. I could also easily see that my companions of that morning were taking the state we were in as if it were something normal. While I lived with every passing second so I might not forget, I was sure they were not noticing. Soon that six-hour incident would just fade into numerous and bigger such incidents that formed part of their lives. This, more than anything else that happened that morning, is what I remember the most. They are what I still live with.

They did not even do anything special, anything out of the ordinary. In the first hour, Tish'ate and Sinnom took turns to jump from rock to rock, ducking whistling bullets, to look for an exit for all of us. The exit was, of course, forward in support of our trapped comrades and not back to save our skins. That attempt was frustrated, so both of them stayed on the open riverbed in front of us, crouching behind rocks and standing guard.

Since we were trapped and in the process of encirclement, anything was possible. We could be wiped out, captured or, with some luck, scrape back to where we had come from without being noticed. I thought the former two possibilities were quite likely. I remember looking at each one of them intently, attempting to discover their internal thoughts and feelings. Were they sharing my worries?

I failed to see any manifestations of fear, panic or preoccupation. I am not trying to romanticize them, this is the truth. I wish I had written about them that morning. I could not figure them out. I could not figure myself out. There seemed to be a big difference between us. Could it be that I loved myself more than they did themselves? Had they developed a method whereby they could hide their innermost feelings and sentiments? I didn't know. They showed nothing to indicate that they were in immediate and imminent danger.

Instead, they started to throw jokes at each other. I cannot remember everything they said but it centered around death and the best way of dying. Joking about death right at its very doorstep may be analyzed in a variety of ways. Psychologists would probably dissect it into mind boggling components. Some would call it desperation, some might analyze it as spite bred of hopelessness, and others would characterize it as external posturing to conceal internal fear. That may earn PhD's, but it would be wrong and misleading.

I am no psychologist, but that morning I observed enough to disagree. In those six hours, I saw acceptance, a calm and serene acceptance of the possibility of death. It was as if, deep inside them, they had come to terms with martyrdom as the best way to show one's love to one's country. True, my companions were amongst the choicest fighters, the best of the best, so to speak. Throughout the three more days of fighting that followed, only three *tegadelti* from our whole company were to be criticized for some form of fear or panic. To be the best amid such a proven pool of courage was no simple matter.

Anyway, they started to joke and I laughed for a greater part of my hours of encirclement. I laughed so much that I sometimes came close to forgetting the situation I was in. They made me laugh, but they also tried to protect me the best they could. Bullets were ricocheting as they hit the rocks and whistling over our heads, crushing all around us. I will never forget how worried they were for my life. Amidst their banter, they would try to squeeze me in their midst so I would not be hit. "Why are you here with us?" they would ask me. I tried to scold them out of over-protectiveness. But they would not listen.

They were most worried about my age. They just would not believe that I could run. They also thought that I would easily succumb to thirst. Several times, they offered me water from their respective canteens. That was an exceptional thing to do under the circumstances. You just never drank water without your leader's permission—not so early in the day, anyway. I had to make all the effort I could muster to turn down the temptation of a sip or two.

So, in lieu of everything that they thought I was missing, they gave me jokes, banter, small talk and laughter. Words like "martyrdom" and "courage" still ring in my ears. This was 1985. The EPLF was fifteen years old that year. Except for Tish'ate and Sinnom, the rest of my companions had joined the struggle in the 1980's. In fact, some had come after Ethiopia's 7th or "Stealth" offensive in 1983. But the comradely concern, the wisdom and the bravery in the face of danger that distinguished the veterans of the Front had already been inherited by these elegant young men and women.

Sometime past one in the afternoon, we were instructed to climb back to where we had started from at the top of the gorge. Once out of our hiding place, the machine gunner saw us and attempted to stop us. We forged upwards all the same. The most dangerous part was crossing the gorge from where we were to where the wounded had sheltered that morning. One by one, we started to cross under the gunner's hail of bullets.

I was fifth in line. Right in the middle of the crossing, I tripped and fell. Bullets were whistling all around me. Where I got the energy to spring up, dart forward and jump to safety, I'll never know. It was a close miss. A bullet made a clean hole at the left hem of my "bell-bottom" trousers. It would have smashed my left ankle.

I will never forget that day. I will certainly never forget Tish'ate, Sinnom, Letebrhan and Wedi Ghirmai. Most of them were about half of my age. Many of them were still children when I joined the EPLF, but they taught me extraordinary things that morning. Their defiance, indeed disdain, for death was phenomenal. I still think and puzzle over it.

" I am not afraid of dying," said Wedi Ghirmai at some point and then added, jokingly, "what I fear is mandible injury. I don't want any bomb or bullet touching my face." I remember glancing at him.

He was good looking.

"What if your leg is amputated?" asked one of the girls.

"I don't mind."

"You self-lover! You want to live after us. You want to see independence!"

It was all said in jest, accompanied by laughter. But it had a tragic twist to it all. Death, in the form of whistling and ricocheting bullets, mortar shells and encircling enemy troops was, after all, everywhere around us. I remember looking at each one of them individually and asking myself which ones would actually see independence.

Many months after that memorable day, when I had gone back to my original place, Arag, Sinnom came to see me. He had gotten married in the meantime and was honeymooning at a place called Halibet, some kilometers away from us. We chatted and laughed a lot. He told me that Tish'ate had died in action, sometime after I had left the unit.

A few days later, Letebrhan and my former platoon's barefoot doctor came to see me and spent a whole day in my place. They had come to attend a course at the School for Cadres, about an hour's walk from Arag. In 1988, after the annihilation of the enemy's Nadew Front and the capture of Afabet, I again met Letebrhan at the new Mes-halit Front. She had now been promoted to platoon leadership. We had a long and nostalgic chat. She told me that Sinnom had died in some battle in '87.

I will never forget Sinnom. I will explain why, later. Let me come back to Letebrhan. In 1990, upon the EPLF's capture of the port of Massawa, I met Wedi Berhe, my platoon leader. In the excitement of the evening of victory, we hugged and kissed on the shores of the Red Sea. He told me that, after 1985, he had married Letebrhan, but avoided telling me where she was. I insisted. With a lot of hesitation and regret, he told me that she too had died in one of the battles between Afabet and Massawa. I sulked and mourned for most of our evening of triumph.

* * *

Let me return to those four days of fierce fighting.

On the morning of our encirclement, all ten or us were lucky to

80

have made it to the relative safety of the top of the gorge, without so much as a scratch. I remember the place as a flat escarpment that was broken in places by sharp-toothed, sun-baked rocks. Wounded comrades being brought from the fighting below were lying under every available shrub, in transit to a temporary battalion clinic further up. I could see that our side had not been having the easiest of times throughout the day.

At about 2 P.M., the ten of us were resting, scattered behind rocks and shrubs when mortar shells started to pound our position. There were no trenches here, nothing to shelter us from direct hits or the fiercely flying shrapnel. The company leader, Bahre Debbas, Letebrhan and one other woman were leaning on a rock some steps above me. " Just sit where you are," he shouted at me. "Don't think of changing places, it won't make a difference. This is where luck and fate decide whom to take and whom to spare. Just stay put." I did just that.

From where we sat, we both tried to guess the number of shells that were falling on that place, the size of a soccer field. For three hours, the bombs rained right, left and center. A couple of times, they fell so close that I could feel the heat. No shrapnel struck me. One that fell a few meters to my right covered me with dust and smoke. Shrapnel flew past me to where Bahre and Letebrhan were. I was sure they were, at least, grazed. I saw them remove dust and continue talking. Some minutes later, Letebrhan was drying some blood oozing from her calf. Some splinters had obviously pierced her flesh. She did not think much of it.

That evening, when it had gotten a bit darker, our company climbed down the gorge, passed our refuge of the morning and was soon running towards the enemy's trenches. The terrain sloped upwards on our left. As we ran, I saw the silhouette of someone running in the opposite direction. "Someone to our left!" I shouted. A spurt of Kalashnikov bullets coming from the silhouette had us all flat on our bellies. One tracer bullet hit the ground about a meter from where I lay. It must have grazed my left buttock as it whistled by. I felt a sharp pain and I shouted, "You're hitting us, damn it!" I thought another company was confusing us for the enemy.

Like Letebrhan that afternoon, I ignored the burning sensation on my left side and continued running. I was to have it treated only four days later. It took months to heal. Anyway, we reached the enemy's trenches without meeting any resistance, formed a line and proceeded further in through a maze of canals leading to the main position. Suddenly, I heard someone exclaim, "*Weyley!*" while firing a bullet at the same time. I was about fourth in line. In the darkness, something at the bottom of the trench obstructed my steps and almost tripped me over. I bent to see what it was. An enemy soldier had just been hit and was dying. A tall man in that narrow canal—I had to step on him to catch up.

The enemy was, at least this time, taken unawares. After his initial successes of the morning and the absolutely crazy bombardment of the afternoon, he had probably thought we would be in no position to attack the way we were. The soldier I had just stepped on had been surprised by Sinnom, who was leading the attack and, in panic, had tried to wrestle him. Sinnom was too quick with the gun and had given him a bullet to the chest. He was giving a dying man's gurgling sound as I passed him.

Sinnom was amazing throughout those four days. From the beginning to the end, he had been going through a most excruciating toothache. Whatever he did—run to attack, shoot or rest—it was with grunts and almost inaudible whines of suppressed pain. Upon the slightest chance of a lull in the continuous fighting, he would crouch on some spot and try to take a nap. But always in vain. If there was a spot to smash with an RPG, he would be called upon to do it. That accomplished, he would lie down somewhere to tend to his pain. But then an assault on an enemy unit would call for his leadership and off he would go at the head of a group of four or five. Again he would collapse in pain....It must have been one long rendezvous with suffering for Sinnom those four days. I had not known or heard about his fighting capacity before that battle. But to me he was the star and the hero of that particular encounter.

When he came to visit me in Arag, I mentioned the toothache to him. "Toothache?" he asked. It took him a while to remember. "Yes, yes, it was in that battle that I had that pain. So much happened afterwards, I got it all mixed up. It is not the pain that I remember most about that battle. It was a nasty battle. Our brigade was not familiar with the Nakfa terrain. The enemy had all the advantage. Such a mean and lowly battle, but it took heroes away from us...."

Among the heroes who perished early the first morning was Assahaita, the lean, handsome and witty company commander who had made me laugh at Nakfa. That evening, as we were resting inside the enemy's trenches, I heard his name being whispered in awe. The next morning, I approached Bahre and asked him about Assahaita. He looked straight into my eyes and said simply, "Haven't you ever heard people say that love in the revolution is never consummated, that it never wears away?" He left me standing where I was, to think over what he had just said. "Death takes away the most beloved" is what he meant. It was his way of telling me that Assahaita had actually been killed.

There is one thing that I always remember about Assahaita, but that I did not mention in my diary. The night before we left Nakfa for Laba, Bahre's wife, who had been in the vicinity of Nakfa, had come to see him. They spent most of the evening in our company.

When Assahaita saw her, he started to tease her with such elegance and hilarity that we were caught in infectious laughter. "How on earth did you know he was in Nakfa?" he kept asking her. "You didn't even take time to come here, did you fly? Couldn't you have delayed yourself somewhere, at least an hour or two?

In the midst of all the banter and roars of laughter, he paused at one point and said, "How about mine? Hasn't she heard that I am here? Would it hurt her to pop in from nowhere?" He was so comfortable with himself, that his feigned self-pity was, I thought, full of grace and dignity. He ended his monologue with the same monotony that I found so funny and attractive under that shade in Nakfa, "Poor, Poor Assahaita, the Poor."

I don't think that he ever got to meet his wife again. How could he? It was early the next morning that we took that long trip to Laba. He was there throughout our stay on top of those mountains. Then, it was back to Nakfa and the battle in whose first few hours he had died. That was one last pleasure and privilege he should never have been denied.

That was also one person whom I wish I had known better. My meetings with him were too short for me to retain more that what I have described here. Nevertheless, he impressed me as a man of a unique combination of humility, courage and flare. He was endowed with wit, kindness, love, seriousness and what many described as an indomitable fighting spirit.

"In a way, it is good that you did not know him so well," a friend of his once told me. "He was a man of integrity, his own man. His death would have crushed you the way it did me."

"Poor Assahaita, the Poor" was rich in spirit.

Assahaita was not the only commander who perished in the course of that four-day battle. Wedi Ghile, the commissar of our company, had moved to replace Assahaita the first day. He too was killed a few hours later. The same afternoon, a jovial man from the Massawa area, Wedi Tza'eda, who had led another company also succumbed to an enemy bullet.

The second day of battle was the most eventful for our company. We had spent the whole day in the enemy's trenches and were scheduled to attack another, more strategic position in the evening. The enemy pre-empted our intentions and attacked instead. It was a stealthy approach following a one-hour blanket bombardment of where we were. Luckily, Wedi Ghirmai was standing guard on the left flank and he felled the first soldier who ventured into the canal. A pitched exchange of fire ensued for about half an hour. The enemy must have seen no point in proceeding. He fell back.

That meant that we had to cancel our planned attack. We spent that night and the next in the same enemy trenches. Company 2 from our battalion had so far been out of the confrontation. It joined us on this, the third day. Some of my students from the Revolution School, including Chu Chu and the artist Hakli, were amongst its number. I went to where they were to see if I could find them. Both of them must have gone on an errand, because they were not there. But I met Almaz from my own department at Arag. Almaz was the one who, along with Oromo, had been first to climb to the top of Mt.Bidho on the morning of our departure from Arag.

I asked her about Hakli, whose real name was Ghirmai Ghebreleul. She told me that he had nicknamed me "Antonio Sabato," the debonair Italian actor of spaghetti westerns. "Antonio Sabato? Why?" I asked her.

"Last night, when you were attacked? Someone told him you were seen moving up and down the trenches with a cocked pistol in your hand."

That was true, but I thought no one had seen me, or that those who did would not tell on me. When the attacking force was repulsed the previous evening, I had moved down the trenches for some chore. At some corner, I saw the body of one of our comrades dangling head down from his firing position. I pulled him down to the ground and turned him round to see who it was. In the process, I saw something hard sticking out of his back. I thought it was a bayonet and, in my panic, drew my pistol out and was about to crouch when someone I did not recognize popped in from around a corner. If he had noticed my behavior he did not comment. When I told him that something was sticking out of the dead comrade's shoulders, he told me that that was not a bayonet in his back. It had something to do with the RPG....I never found out. He must have told Hakli about this. Hakli was one who never passed such golden opportunities for uncanny humor. Apparently, he was having a good time drawing scenes of a spaghetti western with me inside it.

"Tell Hakli to shut his mouth," I told Almaz. "I have been free from any nickname, so far. I don't want to be called Antonio Sabato or even Clint Eastwood at my age!" She laughed. As we talked in the open, the enemy started shelling our position with the same intensity as the previous night. Every time a mortar shell fell, she jumped to protect me. She got so nervous that she led me by the hand to a nearby shelter and told me to go inside.

"How is Hakli and all the others?" I asked her as we shook goodbye.

"They are all right, so far. But then, we just joined you today. I don't like the way this battle is proceeding. You take care of yourself, do you hear?" She squeezed my hand and ran away, ducking to avoid falling shrapnel.

Later on, I found out that in the fierce fighting of that evening, Almaz had carried a wounded comrade on her back all by herself to the safety of the company doctors. On her way back to her unit, she was hit in the head by machine gun fire. She died instantly.

That evening, our company was having a great time with the

enemy. With Sinnom and Wedi Ghirmai leading their groups of "problem solvers," they captured one enemy post after another. Towards morning, the enemy had been dislodged from most of his positions, so that we spent the fourth day at the foot of Mt. Denden. A huge rock that stood erect off the River Hiday was a good spot for our whole company to shelter behind and rest.

I was totally exhausted. My throat was dry and my voice was hoarse and weak. With my sunken eyes and sallow complexion, I must have struck a bewildering figure. The company radio operator took one look at me and said, "How fast you have looked ill," as if seventy two hours of fighting, sleeplessness and going up and down hills was a weekend of pleasure.

Bahre too examined me intently and said, "You've done enough. I'll give you an escort to accompany you to Nakfa. Start immediately."

I refused, of course. I knew enough not to succumb to such temptations, although, deep inside, I was craving for an end to those difficult days. Soon I became the topic. One youngster asked me how old I was. Forty one! He probably could not believe anyone could reach that advanced age. It was about double his and they all died so young. They almost made me feel guilty for possessing sprinkles of gray hair.

The topic shifted to a heated discussion of what the best age was for effective fighting. Some commented on how difficult it must have been for me to suddenly plunge into the battlefield, considering my relatively settled and relaxed life in Arag. I heaved a sigh of relief. It would have been a misfortune if they had thought that I was resenting my being with them, because I was not. I had passed a big test.

I must have dozed off. Sitting beside me, the radio operator, woke me up. He was receiving a message. I overheard him whisper to Bahre, who was also resting nearby—Chu Chu had been killed the previous evening. Public manifestations of sorrow were totally disapproved of. I cringed inside, more in protest then anything else. The cruelty of war has no bounds. I did not know what to do, so I took my notebook out of my jacket and tried to write about this young woman that I had taught and loved like a little sister. My hands would not move. I leafed through the pages back to what I had written when I first saw her at Embalko on 7 August 1985. They are the same words that I have included in this book. I remember closing my eyes and wishing that she had found the time to wash my hair and remove my lice. I don't know what difference it would have made, but in my sorrow, I wished she had.

Again in my sorrow, I remember taking a mental note of the fact that those whom I had written about in my diary, in other words, those who had impressed me most during my two weeks in the trenches were dying one by one. The saying that "the revolution eats up its own children" and that it takes the very best was starting to make sense.

The night Chu Chu died was when we had made dramatic progress on the ground. We had just occupied a hill when mortar shells started to rain on top of us. In the middle of the thunderous noise, I heard Bahre call my name. In the darkness, he pointed to a hill across from us and told me to climb it from our side. "Wedi Berhe is there waiting for orders to attack. Go and join him."

I was so tired that I was in no mood to climb another hill. I protested. He repeated the order firmly and I left without another word. I suspected that he probably did not want me on that hill with all those shells falling almost every second.

My knees were buckling, as if my legs had turned to water, as the Tigrinya expression goes. It was a small hill, but I scaled it on all fours. When I got to the top, I called out Wedi Berhe's name. I found him, Wedi Ghirmai and a few others lying flat behind some rocks. They told me that a whole enemy company was posted some fifty meters away from where we were.

No shells were falling on this position. So, we were a bit relaxed. Wedi Berhe asked me how I was. "Tired," I answered without hesitating, "my knees and legs are no longer mine."

"Same here," he rejoined. "I feel like I am dying, and my leg is in such terrible pain. Let's just grit our teeth. If we finish the company in front of us, we will rest tomorrow. "

We fell silent as we watched the fighting continuing below us. It was a breath-taking show. Fire was flying freely across the sky and in opposite directions as if thousands of meteorites had suddenly been let loose to crisscross and zigzag in all directions. Sometimes, bombs and anti-aircraft rockets would crash headlong in mid-air to explode and splinter into spectacles of fireworks. My eyes were dazzled. Wedi Berhe and Wedi Ghirmai, who could identify types of guns by sound or the angle of the fireballs they let fly, tried to impart to me their amazing knowledge.

But I was in no mood to learn. That night I hated war. With each shot that was being fired, with every exploding bomb, I imagined one Eritrean dying and I resented war. I hated not only the oppressor who was the cause of it all but also those who had invented the murderous weapons of death and destruction that were flashing, burning and exploding right below me.

"I can't believe human folly," I told Wedi Berhe. "I can't believe mankind has created all this just to destroy itself."

Wedi Berhe did not reply. Obviously, it was no time or place for philosophizing. I must have irritated him a little. I dropped the topic but kept thinking about it. That night, I made some final conclusions about the stupidity, cruelty and savagery of man. I was in such a state of agitation that had I maintained it at that level and stayed with those conclusions for much longer, I would probably have gone to the monastery or done some harm to myself. As it happened, I cooled off. I must have rationalized it subsequently as emotions bred in the battlefield. Otherwise, on that night of extreme hunger, thirst, fatigue and the smell of gun-powder, my dazed mind hated humanity.

I dozed off but was startled awake by mortar shells falling in our vicinity. Two or three fell so close that they almost lifted us out of the security of the rocks that were shielding us.

Witty even in this dire situation, Wedi Ghirmai called my name loud enough for me to hear him amid the din of explosions and falling debris. "Just do as I told you the day before. Hide your head between rocks and sacrifice the rest of your body. Don't ever live as a head or a mandible injury."

Wedi Ghirmai was a tested fighter, one of the "problem solvers," as they were known. He was quick, agile and resourceful, which was essential for solving difficult military situations in infantry units. I had heard that he had survived till independence and was looking for him. Only recently did I find out that he had died sometime in the late eighties.

Anyway, his good humor did not spare us the heavy bombardment of that evening. As the shells drew ever closer, my philosophical mood started to change, as did my intense hatred for life and humanity. Instead, I scrambled for cover. Instinct was getting the better of reason and rationality. As I crouched for dear life, I may have called myself, "Liar!"

\* \* \*

We spent the fourth day of battle behind that huge rock at the foot of Denden. It was a quiet day. War has its own rules. Fierce shooting and shelling often stop abruptly and on both sides, without any discernible reason, and it can stay that way for quite a long time. It seems that warring parties just come to temporary truces without so declaring or acknowledging it. It was the same that day and the evening that followed. We were told to sleep around the rock.

However, the quiet and stillness of that night was broken by the incessant howling and hollering of a wounded enemy soldier who had been left behind by his retreating comrades. It had gone on the whole day and continued through the evening. The shrieks were so terrifying that our platoon could not sleep. The man was also pleading, praying for someone to finish him off. We considered bringing him over on a stretcher, but we dropped the idea quickly. The enemy had positioned himself not so far away. We thought that we would be taking unnecessary risks.

In the middle of our debate, our machine gunner, a man of an athletic physique, came up to me and said, straight, "Why don't you kill him with your pistol?"

"How?"

"He is not far away. You can just steal over and give him a bullet."

I was not attracted to the idea, to put it mildly. He could see that I was not about to do it. Apparently, that's what he had expected and wanted. "Give me your pistol then."

"Why?"

"I'll do it," he replied almost begging. "Give it to me, please. I've never killed anyone with a pistol. Besides, he is asking to die. We'll only be relieving him of his pain."

I gave him the pistol and he disappeared into the night. I cannot describe my feeling of the moment. I was definitely participating in a decision to end someone's life—someone who was bound to die in a most horrible way, obviously. All the same, it was a decision. Playing God is so easy in a war.

About to die, the wounded man was still hollering at the top of his voice. "Someone, *Sha'ibia*, all I want is one bullet. Someone, spare me this pain." He had a spine-chilling tone. We heard one pistol shot about twenty meters away. It was followed by a hiccup and silence.

My friend ran back and kneeled beside me. "When you kill with a pistol, you get so close, you know the guy is dead," he told me. I did not say anything. I just took my pistol from him, put it in its holster and lay to sleep. Our machine gunner was a jovial, kind-hearted man who seemed to be everybody's favorite. He would probably never hurt anyone under normal circumstances.

It was a night full of stars. They were fascinating to watch. The stillness of the aftermath of heavy fighting may be as intimidating as the silence just before it. That night seemed peaceful and different. Night guards were assigned and, as if by consent, all of us went into deep sleep.

At about 2 A.M. the sound of volleys of all sorts of gunfire startled our whole company to a sitting position. Some scrambled for their guns, others ran to secure defensive positions. But the shooting was not directed towards us. The sky was lit up with tracer bullets and RPG's exploding in midair.

"Maybe they have captured Barentu," suggested someone from the dark.

"Stop joking," admonished Wedi Ghirmai. "That's impossible!" If it were up to him, the enemy would not have captured Barentu that evening. But it had happened and, therefore, the celebratory volleys into the sky.

We sat where we were, ready for instructions. At about 4 A.M. we were told to move back to our old trenches up on the Denden-Globe-Fidel Pe line. We did just that. The whole purpose of our four-day attack had been to ease the pressure that the enemy had been exerting on Barentu. With Barentu's fall to the enemy, there was no purpose in our continuing.

We reached the top of Globe, to the left of the summit of Mt. Denden, sometime past 6 A.M. Globe is a flat roundish range squeezed between Denden and Fidel Pe, the initial starting point of our company. The first person I found up at Globe was a short and very hairy *tegadalai* named Orit. I paused to chat with him. He expressed to me the deep sorrow that he was feeling upon the loss of his company commander, Assahaita.

"This was one of the worst battles I ever encountered," he told me. "Our company has been totally incapacitated." He seemed to hesitate a little and then said in a sad tone, "Your own boy too is gone."

I did not ask, I knew he meant Oromo, the aspiring artist and sculptor. Tall, handsome and dashing, he had been one of the most popular men in Arag. He liked to joke, never tired of working and had a loud and infectious laughter, audible and distinguishable quite a distance away. He may not have been amongst the best in Arag, but he was making significant progress as an artist when he was so cruelly cut down.

Anyone who climbs Mt. Bidho from Arag and Halibet will probably find the statue of a worker carved into a rock at the entrance of the Anberbeb Area. That statue was carved and put in place by Oromo. In 1982-83, during the Dergue's massive Sixth and Stealth Offensives, Oromo and his friends used to make two to three trips weekly up that steep mountain to work on his project. I hope the statue is still intact.

Even today, ten years on, whenever the Arag crowd gathers, Oromo is sure to be remembered. He was not just an artist and sculptor, he was also endowed with great physical strength and was always there for the numerous chores of the Department. An indefatigable wood-cutter, water-carrier and rock-breaker, he was essential to our little community. He was also simply one of the best volleyball players in the whole Front. His spikes were so accurate, fast and hard to return, that few wanted to play opposite him.

About a week before his death, I had met him at Laba, where our whole battalion had assembled for some form of inoculation. We

91

were standing near the edge of a cliff and I thought the scenery below us would be good for landscape painting.

"Yes, probably," he answered. He had grown up in Ethiopia and spoke Tigrinya with an Amharic accent. I never found out why they nicknamed him Oromo, which is the name of Ethiopia's largest nationality. His real name was Tesfalidet. "What I find fascinating here is the sunset. I have never seen anything like it."

He noticed from my reaction that I had not noticed the Laba sunset and he laughed. "You know, I don't even know whom to talk to anymore," he said jokingly. "A few days ago, I was drinking water at a stream. The sun's reflection was creating some fantastic colors and shapes in the running water. I felt compelled to comment on such rare beauty. A peasant was pouring water some distance away, no one else was there. So I pointed to the jumping waters and the amazing colors and said, 'This is beautiful. Look at it.'

"He must have thought I was crazy. He looked at the reflections, then looked up at the sun and said, simply, 'That's only the sun. The sun is the same, no change!'"

He finished with the Oromo laugh, which the adjacent mountains and cliffs duly echoed. We said goodbye and parted to our respective companies. I had absolutely no idea that I was seeing Tesfalidet Oromo for the last time. Oromo, aspiring painter and sculptor, untiring worker, sportsman and a polite and decent human being....

I left Orit, who himself was to die in some later battle, saddened by Oromo's death. Our company was assigned a place at Globe and I found a nice corner inside a shelter in which to rest. It was a large underground room where Bahre, Wedi Berhe and a few others were also preparing to take a rest. The enemy had not pursued us. There was some time to relax.

Suddenly, someone I had not met before came into our shelter. He was relatively older than most of his comrades. Speaking in a loud voice, he started to complain about an enemy ammunition depot that he had seen down below and that we had left intact. Someone said that it was too late to do anything about it. He would not listen.

He dragged Bahre out of the shelter and, leaning above a canal in the trenches, pointed out the exact location of the depot. It was way down beyond the enemy trenches and almost at the foot of Mounts Kuomintang and Amelto, where enemy soldiers were lodged in.

"You have to give me permission to go down there and destroy it," he told Bahre.

"I can't do that," answered the latter. "The enemy will reoccupy the whole area anytime now. It is too dangerous. Just stay in your place."

The man would not listen. "Listen, we can't just let it stay there. What will it take? I'll be back in half an hour or so. Even if they come, I will be alone and they will not be able to catch me. There is no way I am not going."

It must have been obvious to Bahre that the man would go even if ordered not to. So, he consented reluctantly.

With the enemy far away, we could afford to rise above our firing positions to look. By the time I did so, our gallant fighter had already jumped over abandoned enemy trenches some fifty meters away and was speeding down the slope. I have never observed such happy and unimpeded jumping from rock to rock. In less than ten minutes, he was at the foot of Globe and was speeding towards his target. Bahre had binoculars. We alternated to follow his progress.

We could see him collecting firewood, lighting a fire and throwing torches into what must have been an underground shelter serving as the depot. After some time, another member of the company, a platoon leader named Hagos insisted that he too go down to help. This time, Bahre gave him a communication radio and let him go. Together they proceeded to accomplish their self-assigned mission.

I did not stay long enough to see the explosion. I was eager to find out about Hakli and the others of his company, which was then returning. As I walked towards Denden, I heard a huge explosion from down below.

Maybe I should have seen it, but it does not matter. What mattered to me was the initiative that the man had taken, the type of man that he was. In the short time that I observed him, both before and after his mission, I failed to notice anything distinguishable about him. Another man like all of us. He would wince if pinched and die if mortally wounded. Whenever I remember him, though, I marvel at his courage of that morning. He was going into positions that we had retreated from, fully aware that the enemy was re-occupying it. No one was obliging him to

destroy that depot. On the contrary, his orders were the opposite....
I suppose that, in order to be a hero among heroes, one has to add
a little more to what everyone else does. That morning, my hero did
precisely that.

I regret that I do not remember his name and that I did not try
to find out then. Neither do I know whether or not he is still alive.
On the other hand, the fact that he is nameless is, to me, symbolic.
He is being mentioned here only because I was a witness that day and
I am choosing to write about him. So many heroes of our long struggle—some alive and many more dead—have been lumped together
into a generic mass called "patriots." Brave men and women with
names and faces whose individual and collective feats of courage and
perseverance have made the difference between oppression and freedom are just one mass of martyrs.

There is nothing strange, therefore, in the fact that I do not
remember my hero's name. When I came back from where I had
gone, I found him sitting in the shelter, next to where my things
were. His own mission accomplished, he seemed to have reported
the result to Bahre. He was sewing something, possibly adding
patches to his ragged trousers. I stayed three more days with that
platoon. I heard no more mention of my nameless hero's supreme
act of courage and open defiance of death. I guess it was passed as
another act in a long line of such individual initiatives. No citations,
no commendation, no promotion, no medal of valor...yes, no name.

I said earlier that I had gone to see if Hakli had returned with his
company. I knew he had been in the same unit as Chu Chu. I found
a woman called Birnesh, who was also from Arag, sitting alone and
wiping sweat from her forehead. She had just arrived.

I asked her about Chu Chu and the manner of her death. She did
not say much, but told me that Chu Chu had been worrying a lot
about me. Apparently, she had seen a blood-stained jacket that had
looked like the one I was wearing and had concluded that I had been
hit. I heard her say this with a lump in my throat, swallowing hard
to prevent the tears that were threatening to come. Birnesh was the
one who also told me about Almaz's final moments.

I could no longer postpone my final question. "Where is Hakli?"
I managed to ask. Immediately, her big eyes filled with tears and they

just flowed freely. She nodded slowly. I got up and left full of anger, regret and a sorrow verging on despair.

If it were possible to cry aloud in the revolution, I would have screamed for Hakli. Of the artists that the EPLF was training and raising, Hakli and Michael Adonai were, in my opinion, the most promising. Both were flourishing at an equal pace, although each had his own style and direction.

Once in a while, I would go to their studio in Arag and enjoy watching both of them paint. About 1982 or '83, Hakli was working on one of his famous pieces—the masterpiece of a young girl coming from or going to school. I had become his regular visitor, watching him develop that painting stroke by stroke. I remember now how fully engrossed and totally in contact with his product he would be every time I stole a peek over his shoulder. His concentration in giving shape to the dewdrops on the leaves in the background was so professional no one had any doubt that he would march on to further heights.

"Who is this girl? Who are you thinking about when you draw her?" I asked him once.

"Someone who just came to my mind," he answered.

"You seem to be putting a lot of your own feeling into her," I continued, partly teasing him. "As you grow older, she will be too young for you."

"It is just paint and brush," he replied, pointing to his equipment. "All I need is give her a few touches now and then and make her grow up with me."

At the Revolution School, where I had taught him for several years, he was a naughty boy who always had a quick response to the quickest remark. When he came to the school in 1977, he may have been fourteen. But he had left home to fight not to attend classes. So, while in school, he was always in a constant state of rebellion. As a student, he was one of the best. But he became one of the leaders of a movement called *"Tewzi'e,"* which is Arabic for re-assignment— to the fighting forces, of course. Even then, his wit, sharpness and good nature endeared him to all around him, including us teachers.

One day, in 1978 at the school, most of the older students went on a strike to demand that they be sent to the frontlines. Beraki

Ghebreselassie, who became the Minister of Education and of Information respectively, after independence, was responsible for the EPLF's educational programs. Since all the teachers and officials of the school had given up on persuading our boys and girls out of their demand and determination, the matter passed to Beraki.

He talked to them, pleaded with them and tried to impress upon them the fact that their education and skills would come handy when it came to rebuilding the nation after independence. They listened attentively.

When question time came, one of them got up and said, *"Tewzi'e* is like a disease. It sleeps with us in the evening and wakes with us in the morning. How can we get rid of it?" He was given a long explanation.

Another one got up and said, "We have this big desire to shoot. If you want us to study in peace, then you should allow us to shoot four bullets each from Kalashnikov rifles." Beraki told him that would be the simplest request to fulfill. All of them between twelve to sixteen, the students cheered and whistled for joy. Beraki became an instant hero.

When everything seemed settled Hakli got up to speak. "It is not that we do not like education," he said. "We are willing to study. But, our school here, this place called Zero, is very open to air attacks. We always feel very uncomfortable and insecure here. Four anti-aircraft guns should be planted in each corner so we can feel safe. Otherwise, we will not go back to class...." The appeased crowd lit up again, Beraki's heroism disappeared as instantly as it had come and we all went back to the difficult task of calming down kids who wanted to fight.

At Arag, when he had grown to be about 20, I reminded him of that day and what he had said. He had a mischievous, impish laughter and he laughed it. "Don't you ever forget?" he asked.

"How can I forget? Do you know how much of a bother you were? We are laughing about it now, but you were such a pain, if you care to know."

He laughed once more. "We wanted to fight, you would not let us. We saw you all as obstacles, as some nuisance. We put aside our plans and we came organized, just to put pressure on every teacher.

We won in the end, didn't we?"

Amongst his collection, is the painting of a *tegadalai* rushing to assault an enemy position. With sweat dripping down his cheeks, he is about to break into a fortress or a command post that is up in flames. He holds a bomb in his right hand. While painting it, Hakli had used his own physique for a model. Again, this is telling and symbolic. As his comrades in his company told me later, he had been struck down while rushing an enemy position. They talked quite a bit about his courage and agility.

What touched me most was that Hakli and Chu Chu had died at about the same moment and side by side. On top of all the lovable people I have mentioned in this short tribute to my comrades of the trenches, two fellow students, two children of the Revolution School, two of the students that I had loved and respected most had died. When I left the trenches to return to Arag a few days later, it was with a heavy heart. Chu Chu was right. I had come to Nakfa to bury my children.

# At the Battle of Afabet:
## The Drama of a Piece of Flesh

arch in Arareb was still cool. Temperatures rose in May and became unbearable from June onwards. As members of the editorial board and staff of the EPLF magazine, *Harbenya,* meaning "The Patriot," we were lodged on the sides of a rocky gorge that led up a hill. There were ten of us and each one had a room dug into the ground.

We were physically a part of a larger community that constituted the EPLF's printing press. But since our work required solitude and concentration, we rarely mixed with our noisy and more carefree neighbors. Only rarely would we venture outside our confines, and then only to fetch water or on some such errand.

The 13th of March 1988 started off as any other slow and monotonous day. It stayed that way until about 5 P.M. when our editor-in-chief, Ahmed Al-Keisi called Semere Solomon and myself to our common kitchen. He spoke to us solemnly.

"Both of you are going to Nakfa. It looks like we are about to launch a big offensive there. You are to come back with reports of that battle for our magazine. What you write must measure up to the size and importance of the operation."

On other such occasions, that is, whenever the EPLF was geared to launch an offensive, we would hear some rumors beforehand. We would also make our own deductions from some noticeable and unusual movements. This one must have been a tightly kept secret.

Both Semere and myself had known nothing about it.

"What's the idea?" Semere asked.

"Wa Allahi, I do not have full details. When you get to Nakfa, report to Mesfin Hagos. He is commanding the whole operation. I suspect that this may decide the future of the entire Nakfa Front. At least, that's the feelers I am getting. Keep this to yourselves. There's a car down below ready to take you."

"You mean right now?"

"Aiwa! The radio people have already boarded the pickup truck. Just hurry!"

Typical EPLF. No time for any psychological preparation...you're told and you go. Semere and I ran to our rooms, stuffed our *netsela*, notebooks and ballpoint pens into our bags and ran to where the pick-up truck was. The Toyota was already packed with people from our clandestine radio service up on the mountains, *Dimtsi Hafash* or "The Voice of the Broad Masses" (VBM). We found some space to squeeze on and were soon bumping along with a trail of dust following us. Whenever the truck stopped, the dust would envelop us into a state of frenzied coughing and sneezing. We arrived at Nakfa about midnight.

*Dimtsi Hafash* were sending their best journalists. I now remember Kidane Tsighe, my classmate from high school days. Others were Hassen Sherif, Asmelash Abraha and Wedi Ferej, the video-cameramen. All were big guns at the Information Department. Obviously, everyone was full of anticipation about the nature of our mission. No one, however, said anything about it.

Some months earlier, the enemy had been driven away from his old position at the gates of Nakfa by a lightening EPLF attack. The trenches that he had fortified at Mt. Denden, Globe and Fidel Pe had come under the firm grip of our forces. We had not been called to report on that particular offensive. Even *Dimtsi Hafash* had not attached much importance to it. In fact, Semere and myself had been dispatched to report on that battle days after it had taken place. I remember us taking a relaxed stroll up and down the trenches. The enemy had then been pushed about 20 kms. south of his old positions. He had now built his defense line on the range of mountains called the Amba and the Roret, between the towns of Nakfa and Afabet.

Anyway, when we got to Nakfa, we felt and groped for anywhere to sleep. It was dark and we were all sweaty and dusty. I doubt if any-one slept well that night. I certainly did not—the excitement would not allow it.

The next morning, Kidane from *Dimtsi Hafash,* Semere and myself from *Harbenya* went to the office of Mesfin Hogos to learn about our respective assignments. As I said, he was commanding the whole front and the whole operation. He had just finished conduct-ing a meeting of the division commanders and was seeing them off. He did not make us wait long.

I had met Mesfin several times before, mostly on serious matters. He has always been a man of very few words who goes straight to business after courteous greetings and one or two words of light talk—very consistent. Here is some of what he said, "On Wednesday, the 17th, we will launch an offensive on this front. Our objective is to overwhelm and completely destroy the enemy forces here, cap-ture their weapons and liberate Afabet. Zero-hour is 5 A.M. on Wednesday and our attack will be frontal and on all flanks. If every-thing goes according to plan, we should be at Afabet on the 18th. If, for some reason or some obstacles, we fail to meet that deadline, the operation will be extended by another 24 hours. We should be at Afabet on the morning of the 19th. If we are not, then we will abandon the whole operation and make a try another time."

The three of us were listening to him attentively. "If, as we expect, our offensive goes according to plan," he continued, "it will be a major defeat for the enemy. None of his weapons can escape our capture or destruction. The result will tip the strategic balance in our favor. I am sure you understand the implications."

"If the operation succeeds, is there the intention or possibility of pursuing the enemy beyond Afabet?" we asked.

"No," Mesfin replied calmly. "We will hold Afabet and build our defenses probably at Mes-halit. We have no intention of pursuing the enemy. Our whole purpose here is to completely destroy the enemy's Nadew Front and then to preserve and protect our gains. Since the enemy's losses will be tremendous, we will shift to the defensive while closely following the repercussions to the enemy of his imminent defeat. We will also weigh international reaction to our victory."

Without saying more, he handed us three pages of typed writing and said, "This explains the whole operation. Read it and I'll be back to answer any questions you might have." He left the room.

I have since lost the notebook in which I jotted down the main contents of the paper. I do remember, however, that it gave in very brief form, a detailed account of the number of fighting units on both sides, the corresponding troop positions, the balance in arms and ammunition and the supply lines. The paper also indicated the time, positions and line of attack of the EPLF and gave details of the manner and speed with which each division was expected to progress towards its assigned goal. Since the aim was also to encircle the enemy completely, another division was to be placed at Mes-halit, thus blocking the enemy's only escape from Afabet to Keren.

It was a simple and uncomplicated plan, not difficult to understand. To me, it looked like a simple problem of addition—two plus two equals four.... The enemy had, of course, more troops—some 20,000 strong. Our side had slightly more than half of that. But that was not seen as a problem since the EPLF had always had to confront troops four to five times its size. What amazed all of us was the utter simplicity of the whole plan and the daring behind it. "We should finish by 24 hours, if not, by 48..." was a remark that we kept repeating among ourselves. Mesfin came back to us as we were debating the practicality of the operation.

"Any questions?" he asked as he sat.

"Well, what can we say? We are just wondering if all this is practical."

He smiled. "That's the plan. We shall see the result together. The information you now have has only been shared with division commanders. Even brigade commanders have not been included in the secret. You are to keep what you have heard only to yourselves. You will be assigned to the different command posts. Semere, you will be with Witchu all the time, that's the left flank. In fact, he's leaving right now, so go with him. Kidane, you will be at the central command post, where I will be. Alemseged, go see Ali immediately at the offices of Division 61. They will be on the central flank. Goodbye and good luck."

Semere left with Witchu, the commander of the 85th Division, some minutes later.

\* \* \*

That afternoon, I went to the office of the 61st Division. Luckily I found the Commander, Ali Ibrahim, and the Political Commissar, Adhanom Ghebremariam, chatting under the shade of a tree. I knew them both quite well. Ali had joined the EPLF about a month before me, in late 1974. I met him at the training camp in Bahri Bara where he was leading a platoon of trainees. He formed part of a group of university students that had included such famous fighters as Teklu Mesfin, Petros Methusalah and Amanuel Fessehaye. The latter was from the same neighborhood in Asmara as myself. Three of them were to make good names for themselves before they died in different encounters with the enemy.

By the time we joined the training camp, all four had acclimatized themselves to becoming soldiers. I remember noting that they were already *tegadelti*. That was not easy for city boys like themselves. I got to know Ali and Teklu Mesfin better than the others. They would come over to our platoon and share their limited experience at the training camp with us.

I had also known the Division Commissar, Adhanom, from 1975. After the cessation of hostilities between the EPLF and the ELF that year, Adhanom had been put at the head of a group of *fedayeen* constituted from both Fronts. I met him first at a village called Embeito, about 20 kms. south of Asmara, when I went on one of my first errands as a *tegadalai*. We had the same type of long, almost straight hair and sported a similar bushy beard and mustache. He had been the veteran and, when I joined the Front, a lot of people thought that I was his brother. When he saw me at Embeito, he broke into a smile and said, "You must be my long lost brother, Alemseged." I embraced him and said, "And you must be my long lost brother, Adhanom." We became friends.

"Why are you here?" Ali asked good-naturedly as I shook hands with them under the shade.

"Didn't Mesfen Hagos tell you? I've been assigned to your command for the operation."

"What do you mean our command? What for?" He did not seem to like the idea.

"I've been told to report on the progress of your flank. You know, to write for our magazine...."

"Out of the question. I don't see the purpose of such adventures. If you want to write, stay around here and follow events with our staff. You can then interview us after the operation."

Adhanom was quiet at the beginning. Ali's tone had such a finality to it that I began to fear I was about to be denied the opportunity. I protested.

"Don't take it personally," said Ali in a persuasive manner, "Our initial post will be Mt. Itahalbeb. The enemy will know that we will be commanding from there. There is no doubt that he will bombard it with artillery and jet-fighters. I cannot permit you to be there with us. You are not going to endanger your life for an article in a magazine."

"Let him go," Adhanom intervened for the first time.

"Come on, you know what it will mean," Ali retorted quickly.

Adhanom smiled and said, "If they bombard us we'll squeeze him under some rock or hide him in a hole. We can't turn him back from here....Just come back tonight and have dinner with me," he continued turning to me. "I'll also give you a room in which to sleep."

Ali agreed reluctantly. Until the end of the battle for Afabet, Ali never stopped worrying about my safety. I found that very touching.

I stayed and relaxed in Nakfa for three days. On the afternoon of the 16th of March, we were told to move towards the field of battle. For about half an hour, we traveled by car. From the western foot of the old trenches around Denden, we left our cars and started walking down the winding road that leads to Afabet. Fidel Pe, the trenches that I had fought in, in August '85, were to our right as we passed them. Ali, Adhanom, a part of their staff, the operators and Hassen Sherif from *Dimtsi Hafash* and myself were all walking together.

"We look like a whole unit from a platoon. They may see us from Amba over there," said one pointing to the mountains visible from a long distance.

"Let them see us," replied Adhanom, "They cannot suspect anything. They'll probably think we are on some insignificant errand."

The whole week, Nakfa had been hosting a sports contest involving whole battalions and brigades to divert the enemy's attention from the other preparations being effected under his very nose. Since these activities were reserved for the night, even those who had been informed about the operation could discern almost no manifestations of an impending major battle.

We talked all the way to Itahalbeb. Everyone in our team had a story to tell about the area we were treading. This is when I realized that practically every gorge and ravine, every rock and boulder had fascinating stories to tell. Ali had commanded the front almost from the beginning, in 1979. He was telling most of the stories. His staff and operators would enrich his bits and pieces by adding interesting details, the names of fallen comrades and some funny anecdotes.

It was a long walk, but the discussion kept us so entertained that we were at the foot of Itahalbeb before we even knew it. Incidentally, no one uttered a word about the big event of the next morning. Had I not been informed by Mesfin Hagos, I would have been an ignorant fellow-traveler to all those superbly mysterious and secretive companions of mine.

The ravine and open space leading up to Itahalbeb was fully occupied by one or two brigades frantically moving around in earnest preparation. Everything had obviously been put in place. But companies and platoons needed to check and double check their weapons and their troops' basic supplies. I felt like I was inside a highly mobilized anthill.

We took a rest and drank some water. After a while, the men and women of the brigade started to assemble some fifty meters from where we were. Their commander, Tekle Manjus, meaning Little Tekle, asked me to come along to attend the meeting.

I tried to take some notes on what he said to his eagerly awaiting men and women. A few sentences into his speech, though, he told them the purpose of the offensive. Immediately the ravine broke into an electrifying roar and applause. The women ululated. It was such a genuine and spontaneous expression of joy that Tekle Manjus found it difficult to calm his troops down so he could continue. They hardly heard his advice and directions about the caution and military discipline he expected of them.

It was a happy occasion. Everyone was soon hugging and congratulating each other. Obviously this was the culmination of years of patient waiting and defensive fighting in the trenches and foxholes of Nakfa. Each had probably vowed to take revenge every time he or she buried a comrade, a friend or a lover. It was time not just for a strategic gain, but also for personal fulfillment, even personal vendetta.

Two acquaintances from my days at the Revolution School and at the Information Department, a woman called Tirhas Habte and Wedi Kidane, spotted me from a distance and came over to say hello. They were surprised to see me with the commander of their brigade. They were probably wondering what military credentials had placed me in that company. They joked a little about it. Both of them had absolutely no doubt about the success of the offensive. "Tomorrow?" Tirhas said, "Tomorrow is going to be a feast...." She is still alive. Wedi Kidane, an urbane and funny man, was killed the next day, somewhere between Ithalbeb and Ad Sherum.

Towards evening, we climbed Itahalbeb. All mountains confuse me, but never the way Itahalbeb always does. When you look at it from Mt. Denden, it looks like an ice-cream cone overturned. From other angles, it takes totally different shapes. We were on top of it at about 6 P.M.

Itahalbeb had changed hands several times over the years. The last time, when the enemy was still around Denden, it had been under his control. The foot of the cone-shaped summit of the Itahalbeb was where we stopped. There was not too much space for the kind of elaborate trenches one saw elsewhere. Except for the side we took to climb, Itahalbeb is frighteningly slopy and slippery for the most part. On some edges, the slopes fall sharply to form cliffs and precipices. Under normal circumstances, monkeys make their homes up where we were.

Amongst all the rocks was a shelter where we put our bags and things. We then walked over to the trenches to enjoy the sunset and to gaze at the enemy positions sprawled before us, still a considerable distance away. It was getting dark, but not quite. Except for our low voices and shuffling feet, the evening was quiet. I can still hear that silence. As it grew darker and our voices changed into whispers, I remember the hush getting louder and more intimidating. Writers often say that absolute silence has its own voice. They are right. For me, at least, the quiet of the night before the Battle of Afabet was deafening.

By about nine, we had eaten dinner. We went into the shelter to lie down and get some sleep. The shelter had a quadrangular shape, but its breadth was too narrow, not wide enough to stretch one's legs in full. It had enough length to cram four of us. I went in first. Then Adhanom, Ali and Hassen Sherif of *Dimtsi Hafash*. We talked some, exchanged a few jokes and smoked cigarettes.

They looked so relaxed and free of worries that I felt compelled to ask them. "Aren't you supposed to have the jitters of the night-before-battle?"

"Our task is practically over," answered Ali. "We have laid out and handed over our plans to the executors. All we need to do now is just supervise."

I fell asleep. When I woke up in the middle of the night, I heard them talking. They were also smoking cigarettes. "Hey, are you still awake? Why don't you get some rest?"

"I guess you were right," came Adhanom's voice, "The jitters have finally invaded us. Besides, you've been snoring."

"What do you expect? I've been all cramped up here...." I guess one never admits to drunkenness and snoring.

We talked some more and smoked quite a few cigarettes. I dozed off again.

\* \* \*

I must have fallen into very sound sleep. I did not hear them leave the shelter. I started up only when something exploding near-by shook our shelter and almost threw me against the wall. I sat up very angry with myself. As a war correspondent, I had meant to capture the first few moments before zero-hour. I groped in the dark and found my sandals, my bag, pistol and notebooks and rushed towards the command post.

It was still several minutes before 6 A.M. The sun was not yet up, but it was light enough outside. The operators had their radios on. No codes during battles, it is all straight talk. Commanders were already busy giving instruction and receiving feedback from their subordinates.

Ali was sitting on a rock at one edge of Itahalbeb, firing orders into his radio. Adhanom was also holding a radio and listening intently to the maze of voices, commands, explanations, and arguments that were already filling the quiet of the morning. The shooting seemed to come from all corners—right, left, front and even behind, obviously, from our heavy artillery units.

Half an hour or so into the battle, it started to become clear that Itahalbeb was, after all, not going to be targeted, as Ali had feared. First, because our men and women of the central flank had taken the enemy's first line of defense by complete surprise and totally controlled it within a few minutes. Secondly, our attack had been all-sided, spreading simultaneously from the Red Sea coastal plains to the mountains of Rora. It had all been carefully studied and planned. The enemy had not been forewarned and, in many cases, was forced to abandon his first lines of defense either totally routed or with his numbers decimated in a lightening attack.

Even I could easily understand, from what I was hearing on the communication radios, that that had been the case. I heard Witchu, commander of the 85th Division, say on one of the radios, "Are you slicing and peeling them from their positions? Just keep slicing and peeling!" Witchu was of peasant origin, one who rose through the ranks to where he was. He is still one of the major figures of the Eritrean Army. He always has had a way with words. I looked at a radio operator and he said, "The 85th is doing fine. Witchu is happy."

Bits of information were starting to come in. One position captured here. A tank burned, so many prisoners of war captured.... I started to jot what I heard in my now lost notebook. But, from that early stage, I started to suspect that my journalist's errand might not succeed after all. The whole battle was so big, so fast and efficient that, as the morning wore on, I started to find it difficult to understand and cope with its speedy progress. Commanders and operators alike used code-names to call each other. So, although I stayed close to Ali most of the time, I failed to get a clue as to whom he was addressing and to which angle of the flank. Busy as he was, I did not even think of asking him. Adhanom was more relaxed and approachable that morning. He had begun to explain some things to me, but he left us before noon to go forward, probably to where the brigade commanders were.

So, I sat with the radio operators. Several big and smaller communication radios turned on, the din they created was totally confusing. "Enter Venus...out Rora": calm commands, fast and sometimes angry instructions, panting voices heralding a gain, someone pleading for re-enforcement from hills, riverbeds and ravines.... I could not believe that an organized and coordinated battle was being directed from our hilltop. One of the operators must have read my puzzled mind. He said to me, pointing towards Ali, "Don't worry, it's his problem."

I sat with them for a great part of the late morning. Positions were identified by number, that is, by their elevation. "1728 has been captured," says one. "Great!" exclaims another. I would ask what exactly 1728 was. Someone would point to a hill far beyond and say, "That one," and just go on with his chore. A war correspondent must acquaint himself with every twist and turn of a battlefield, I remember thinking to myself. If not, he must be good at map and contour reading. Ali's aides brought a military map and tried to explain the whole battle to me. I grasped just a little, not much. Even in my high school geography lessons a long, long time before, contour reading had been one of my chief antagonists.

A war correspondent should also be an obstinate and unflinching inquirer, one who keeps coming back even when rebuffed. I tried that a couple of times and I got a couple of polite answers. But everyone was so engrossed in whatever he was doing that I started to restrain myself. Besides, I did not like the idea of someone telling me to let him do his job. So, by about 9 A.M. I had put my notebook back into my jacket and gotten more interested in the faces and voices of my companions and in the trenches of Itahalbeb.

Reports of one gain after another kept coming in. It was becoming obvious from everyone's face that the momentum the offensive had taken from the start was not about to slow down. I stopped bothering about the statistics of captured enemy soldiers and all sorts of heavy weapons. The whole thing, the possibility of such a huge victory simply awed and almost intimidated me. I kept recalling the plan that Mesfin Hagos had shown us a few days before. I felt as if I was actually watching its arithmetical simplicity moving towards a simple solution—two and two adding up to four

I had another notebook where I registered my personal observations and feelings. I still have it. At 10:30 A.M. the same day, I wrote the following:

> Mist is covering the ground and the heights around me. I have now come back to the shelter to write this. Bees are buzzing and whining all around me. I don't know where they came from. I hope they don't bite me. Compared to all the shooting and booming around me, their threatening sound is music to my ears.

> This is my first time to watch EPLF division commanders in real action. One learns a lot from such an opportunity. First, their thorough knowledge of the topography in this area enables them to understand the situation of every unit under their direction. They don't even need maps, which I see Ali referring to only in case of confusion. Secondly, I notice that they do not take time or hesitate in making decisions. All I hear from subordinates is attentive listening, maybe a question or two and a quick agreement. I am yet to hear anyone in a state of panic or argument.

> "Don't worry about the one to your right," I heard Mesfin Hagos's instructions some minutes ago. "If they are resisting, just clear the positions to the right and left and isolate them. Proceed to the next target."

> "I understand," came the reply.

I thought that a bit odd. I found Adhanom preparing to leave Itahalbeb and go forward. "Why is Mesfin Hagos telling someone to isolate enemy positions and just go forward? Does it mean that our comrades are leaving enemy troops behind and proceeding?

"This is an offensive of annihilation, of total disintegration and rout," Adhanom responded. "If the enemy resists, you just do not

110

waste time and men. As Mesfin just said, you clear his wings and isolate him. You may leave a platoon to stand guard, just in case.
Isolated troops, no matter their number are of little effect. In this
manner, you cut off the enemy's lines of communication and cohe-
sion. You'll see, we'll be collecting surrendering groups and individuals as we go."

"They won't be a threat from the rear?"

"Their morale is already hitting rock-bottom. They will not have
enough spirit for that kind of reaction."

My knowledge of our commanders, both individually and as a
group, has always been limited to periods of peacetime and mostly
from some distance. I found now that their life in war was dramatically different from what I had seen and heard previously during
such periods. At 4 P.M. I wrote the following about them,

> Their responsibility is truly heavy. Over 10.000 tegadelti are
> involved in this battle alone. This means that the ultimate
> responsibility for the safety of these 10.000 falls squarely on
> the shoulders of these commanders. Besides, they are lead-
> ing a battle that will probably play a decisive role in the
> future of the entire nation and people of Eritrea. How
> dreadful if they were to commit a mistake? How worried
> they must be about setbacks that may be traced back to
> some defective planning or a misguided command on their
> part?
>
> An aura of glory and mystique generally accompanies
> the war commander or the war hero. We rarely realize this,
> but our commanders are defeating full-fledged generals,
> including West Pointers and Sandhurst elites. We don't call
> our commanders that, but they are, themselves, generals. So
> they are usually regarded and treated with respect and some
> awe. They too do not refrain from showing off their celebri-
> ty status and privileges by the way they live and behave.
>
> In an egalitarian community like ours, such behavior
> stands out as odd and is frowned upon. But I guess I am com-
> ing to understand or, at least, just coming to terms with their
> style. They are, after all, soldiers who always put their lives on

the line, as I see them do now. Theirs is a life of danger that may simply end any moment. Should they be blamed for enjoying it while it lasts?

I wish to God that they win tomorrow and we enter Afabet! I hope there's stuff there to celebrate with. I'll just let loose and go on a spree! I haven't even seen an empty bottle of beer in fourteen years!

The battle proceeded very well. However, by early afternoon, it had become clear that the 24-hour schedule was not to be met. Some position to our left had not been captured as planned. The intention had been to stop the enemy's retreat at Moga'e, a seasonal river about half-way between Nakfa and Afabet. It had not worked.

"So, what happens now?" I asked Ali, when he came to the shelters in early afternoon to eat something and drink tea. He took the tea and refused the food. It looked like he was surviving on cigarettes alone.

"They will be annihilated, no doubt about that," he answered. "But not tonight. We'll be in Afabet the day after tomorrow—very early."

At 5 P.M. we were ordered to climb down the slopes of Itahalbeb. We were to follow the traces of the combatants who had pushed the enemy some 20-30 kms. away from Amba and its adjacent positions.

I would not want to pass a puzzling thing that I saw at Itahalbeb. As soon as we climbed it the previous night, I had been startled to see some eight or nine human skulls neatly arranged and placed on a long, flat rock. This had been the enemy's position. No doubt, he had placed them up there.

"What is all this?" I asked one of the intelligence men of the division, who happened to be close by.

"The Dergue does strange things," he replied. "In order to toughen his men, he tells them that revolutionaries do not get buried, they are just eaten by hawks. But these are the remains of soldiers that we, ourselves, killed."

I did not understand the logic. I still find it hard to accept. I doubt if anyone, except perhaps shepherds, have ever climbed Itahalbeb after us. The skulls may still be there.

\* \* \*

A Toyota pickup was waiting for us at the foot of Itahalbeb. We boarded it and were soon speeding in the direction of Afabet. Some kilometers on and signs of the magnitude and ferocity of the day's battle started to show. Corpses of enemy soldiers were everywhere. So were small and large groups of captured soldiers.

The smell of victory was all around us. Even the air seemed to herald it. The Toyota twisted and turned through the dry Hidai riverbed, which doubles as the road to Afabet. We passed one fiercely burning tank somewhere. Another one, with its top, including the muzzle of its gun blown off some meters away, almost blocked the road. In about an hour, we were at the foot of one of the Roret Mountains.

We left the car and started climbing up a steep slope. I think the name of that particular mountain was Hartetet. It too had a number. I wanted to see how far up I could keep pace with Ali, so I followed him.

"Hey, don't strain yourself, you'll get tired," he said to me without looking back. "The supply personnel and their donkeys are coming at a slower pace. Why don't you take your time and come with them."

I refused. As we climbed, he talked about the EPLF's strategic retreat in 1978. He pointed to some hill visible from where we were—it was his head quarters for part of the time. The strategic retreat, effected when the Ethiopians, helped massively by the Soviet Union, pushed the EPLF from around Massawa and the highlands, had been a gradual process. The Front had taken full advantage of all available strategic positions to delay the enemy's advance and to weaken his strength at every opportunity. Serious damage had, therefore, been inflicted on his morale and material capacity at such famous encounters as Elaber'ed, Tsebab, Gonfolom, Mes-halit, Ma'imide and here, to the north of Afabet, around Ad Sherum and the Roret Mountains. By the time the EPLF built its durable trenches at the Nakfa Front, the enemy had been deprived of thousands of soldiers, scores of tanks had been destroyed or captured and, basically, he had been drawn into a trap. After ten years of a bitter contest of wills and eight unsuccessful large scale enemy offensives, it was time for the EPLF to go for the kill. Ali had played an important role in this ten year long defense of Nakfa which had been under siege since 1978.

"You know," he said, "there is no mountain, valley or gorge here that we did not climb and descend to search for a suitable defense line. Don't remind me of the retreat! We had no time for anything. Everywhere we went the enemy would follow. We had no time to breathe! We climbed up Mt. Denden only after having weakened her here." Fighters had the habit of referring to the enemy in the female gender. More because they knew it irritated the other side than anything else.

He also described to me the EPLF's 1979 "initiative." This took place after the enemy's 5th large scale offensive had been frustrated. That offensive had been yet another bitter contest for the capture of Nakfa. Late in '79, EPLF fighters had descended from their positions at Nakfa, pushed the enemy down from his trenches and, by penetrating deep behind enemy lines, established a temporary base area inside his own territory. By thus attacking his strongholds from the back and capturing or destroying his artillery units, ammunition depots and communication lifeline, they had pushed him back to the area where we were that evening. It was an operation that had played a decisive role in proving, beyond reasonable doubt, that not only was the EPLF a potent defensive force, but that it also had the ability to go on the offensive, given the time and the logistical supply.

After around a half-hour of fast climbing, I started to fall back. He was, of course, in a hurry to get to the top and start communicating. My heart was about to burst. So, I slowed down. By the time I got to the top, it was getting a bit darker. Ali was already busy with this radio.

I prefer climbing to descending. The breeze on top is always refreshing. It has a resuscitating power. It gives one time to wonder how one ascended from down below to up above. I guess one's ego too is fed a little.

We did not eat much. About nine of us, mainly the commanders, their top aides and myself lay down in a line to get some sleep. There had been a battle on where we were, sometime in the morning.

Bodies of Ethiopian soldiers were scattered around us. In fact, a dead Ethiopian was some eight to ten meters away from where I was lying down at the edge of the line. I was too tired to bother.

"Is this place properly searched? We should watch out for stray enemy soldiers. There are hundreds around", warned Beghe, the division's artillery commander. No one replied. In minutes, we were all in deep sleep.

Late at night, we heard the sound of a short, but quite intense exchange of fire, mainly from Kalashnikov rifles. The sound came across the valley to our right. "What was that?" I asked. "Probably stray soldiers, I told you..." replied Beghe. We all went back to sleep.

The next morning, March 18th, the day started with yet another fierce battle. The positions that had delayed our advance were soon captured. Adhanom had re-joined us in the meantime and we were told to move to another mountain in front of us. It may have been around 10 A.M. The Sahel sun was already in full force. Enemy planes were all over the place. The two mountains were connected by ridges and escarpments, so that we did not have to go down to the bottom of where we had started. At one point, two jet fighters came so low above us, that they sent us scattering right and left. They did not fire at us, though. They were probably interested in something else— maybe artillery positions or tanks.

Even from the connecting ridges and escarpments, the mountain we changed to had a steep slope to climb—maybe a half hour of fast paced walking. Beghe, Hassen Sherif of *Dimtsi Hafash* and myself were too slow for the rest. Above all, the sun was merciless.

"Damn it, let's take a rest," said Beghe. Hassen and I took that as enough excuse to seek the nearest shade and snuggle beneath a rock. After all, Beghe was the soldier among us. Fighting was going on ahead of us, but we just sat immobile for quite a while.

Beghe is a native of Semhar, in the Red Sea areas of Eritrea. A veteran of the Eritrean revolution, he is a lot of fun to be with. As we rested, I took the opportunity to ask him about how our tank and artillery units had been faring up to that moment. He had his radio and was still communicating with his subordinates. He told me what he could remember. He also gave me a list of the enemy tanks our side had destroyed or captured. I registered every thing in my notebook. About noon, we struggled and sweated to the top of the mountain.

The summit was a narrow, flattish place, probably not more than 2500-3000 square meters in area. It was a heavily fortified place and had obviously been the scene of very heavy hand to hand fighting just a few hours before we had come. Some 30-40 bodies of Ethiopian soldiers lay only on one edge of the summit. They were fresh corpses. In some cases, their blood had not quite dried. I paused to stare at the bodies of our enemy and was surprised to find that the sight that confronted me did not make me happy. Instead, I was seized by a gush of compassion for those young human beings so uselessly wasted.

I started to walk around, investigating the enemy's trenches. Someone warned me to stick to where we were. "Some of them may be pretending to be dead," he told me. So, I took some care as I strolled about. At first, what amazed me was what our fighters had done. Except for the side we took while we came up, the remaining approaches to the summit were just cliffs and sharp falls. How they climbed up to do what they had done I could not figure out. Upon climbing up such terrain, one would want to rest. Maybe it had to do with the adrenaline that battles are supposed to stimulate. My comrades climbed up those slippery and stiff elevations that morning and simply finished off every enemy soldier they encountered on top. Most of the bodies were lying on the back, facing the sky. Most were hit on the head, on the face or the chest. They did not seem caught in general exchanges of fire, in volleys and crossfire where one cannot know whose bullet hit whom. Excellent marksmen aiming and hitting their target had clearly finished them. It seemed that no bullet had been wasted.

I tried to put myself in the position of the dead soldiers and imagine their ordeal of that morning. It was as if they had been waiting there just to die. I tried to imagine the very ordinary and ever so congenial men and women of our fighting forces coming to put these pathetic corpses in the position they were. Human beings living and breathing just a few hours before were now lowered to grotesque postures. I pictured them falling to bullets, possibly fired by people I knew, that were doing clean and terminal work. I shuddered, awestruck by the merciless, annihilating mood my own com-

116

rades must have entered in the course of that battle.

I often think of that mountain top in symbolic terms. There I felt that I actually saw in the corpses the hatred that my comrades bore against alien rule and oppression. I also saw the extent to which they would go to consummate their love for freedom. For this was hand to hand combat, not artillery or tank units finishing the enemy off from a distance. Here I could see the action and the result of human anger terminating the life of another human. At one point, I remember saying to myself, "God have mercy! Never put me at the other end of my own comrades!" And I trembled again.

From that moment on, I decided, once again, to stop wasting my time on the battlefield reports that kept on coming. Numbers, even of strategic weapons being captured, stopped making any sense. Statistics, I concluded, could never describe the phenomenon that was the *tegadalai*. What would it mean to say, for example, that I saw scores of bodies on one limited section of the summit I climbed on the 18th? In any case, if I were to interview everyone of the *tegadelti* that morning, they would probably have told me that they had found no joy in killing. So, I felt it would be unfair to be satisfied with a mere report of a battle and all the cruelty and abnormality that characterize it. There is more, I told myself, to a *tegadalai* than what he does or is done to him on the war front.

Our revolutionary culture is still very poor in discussing and describing individuals and individual acts of courage and heroism. Unless we do that, the *tegadalai* will never get his due, and his or her greatness will never be known. We keep using very general and lofty terms to define the collective. One hears about perseverance, tenacity, grit and fortitude as characterizing the spirit of *tegadelti*. I find such words extremely limiting and an obstacle to describing what the life of *tegadelti* constitutes. There is no life in those words, no pain...and pain in all its forms—the process of overcoming or suppressing it—is what makes the *tegadalai*. True, the corpses in front of me were the result of the unflinching courage of my comrades, the courage to jump into the lion's den and tackle him by hand. What about the pain, though? The deaths, the fears denied, the hatred for blood, the compassion even for the enemy?

We stayed on the summit until about 5 P.M. Ali had left us much earlier to join his brigade commanders up front. I went down with Adhanom. He led me through steep slopes and falls that seemed previously untrodden by human feet. I had said earlier that one of my worst antagonists during the struggle had been going down a mountain. Independence came without me ever mastering the art of descending.

As he jumped from rock to rock with amazing ease, Adhanom shouted backwards and said to me, "Step lightly on the rocks. Be careful, some loose stone might take you down with it." Soon, he was down and out of my sight. The way I landed my feet was awkward and heavy. Not just loose stones—I could uproot even those firmly in place. By the time I joined Adhanom across the Hidai River, I had fallen and rolled over twice, my trousers had been torn and I had been scratched and bruised all over. Adhanom gave me a mischievous grin. I did not show it, but I was quite angry with him.

What surprised me about Adhanom was that when he had left us at Itahalbeb the previous morning, his operator had succumbed to sunstroke in some wilderness. They had no water on them. Adhanom, too, had come near collapse. They got help only late in the afternoon. It was after having recovered from that ordeal that he had led me down that terrible descent.

We had come to a shelter that the wounded were using as a transit stop before going on to the hospital. The person in charge gave us some water, food and tea. I do not recall that person's name, but he left me with something to remember him by.

As we sat resting, we saw quite a number of captured soldiers being led towards the riverbed. They had apparently been kept in some gorge above.

"Where did these come from?" asked Adhanom.

"They were cut off on that hill to our right. We went up there last night and attacked them. They surrendered after a short fight," said the *tegadalai* in charge.

"Who went up there?"

"Six comrades were resting here. They had brought a wounded comrade on a stretcher. We agreed to go up and attack. That's all."

"Who told you to leave your wounded here and go to fight? You just do what you want?"

118

"*Mbwa!* Who would tell me to do anything? I am in charge here. We knew they were up there. We were afraid they might come down and finish us and our wounded off. We got the better of them."

"All right, we will see about that. How many were there?"

"About 57 or 58. We stole close to the guard, threw bombs, shot full rounds and made a lot of noise. They thought we were a whole company and started jumping out of their trenches individually and in groups. I think we killed only two. Didn't you hear some shooting last night?"

Adhanom admonished him for having strayed from his assigned duty, even though what he had done was laudable. But I could see that, deep inside, he was impressed by the young barefoot doctor. Most of the victories of the EPLF became possible because such individuals put their own lives at stake for whatever they saw as a gain for the revolution. Adhanom told me of a couple of other such examples of initiative and courage beyond the call of duty.

There was still time before proceeding further towards Afabet. So, in order to fulfill my journalistic duties, I walked to where the prisoners were and started to talk to them. They were all, obviously, of peasant stock. Most of them were incoherent and knew very little of what they had been fighting about. I asked if there was anyone who could explain things better. One got up, stood at attention and said in Amharic, "I can, sir. I am a sergeant and, above all, a member of the Worker's Party of Ethiopia."

I took him aside and asked him what the situation in Ethiopia looked like. He did not even give me time to open my notebook. "That Shankilla is playing at the expense of the Ethiopian people," he blurted out. "Shankilla" is the name of a nationality in Ethiopia. He was, obviously, using it in a derogatory sense.

"Who is the Shankilla?"

"Menghistu Hailemariam." the prisoner answered. I detested him immediately.

"What kind of a traitor is this?" I asked their guard. "How can he betray his leader so quickly?"

"That's how they all are," he replied. "They just squeal even when not asked."

I did not ask the sergeant another question. I left him where he was and went back to Adhanom. Soon we had boarded our Toyota pickup and were speeding towards Afabet.

* * *

Ad Sherum is the only pass by road, north of Afabet. When the first plan of cutting the enemy off at the Moga'e failed, he had collected all his remaining men and materials and attempted to retreat through Ad Sherum into the wide and open plains of Afabet. Had he succeeded in doing so, it would have been possible for the enemy to use his tanks and heavy artillery for more effective defense. It did not work that way.

That afternoon, the Ad Sherum pass was a rare and horrendous sight. By the time we stopped some kilometers short of its approaches, Ad Sherum had made it into the history books. From that distance, it looked as if all the hills, rocks and vegetation in its environs had gone up in flames. A volcanic eruption could not have wreaked so much destruction.

A few hours earlier, about seventy tanks and trucks carrying or pulling missiles and ammunition and heavy artillery weapons had tried to escape through the narrow pass. These had been the remnants of the many more that had either been captured or destroyed. One of the EPLF tanks that had been following the convoy in hot pursuit stopped at about where we had reached and aimed its 100 mm gun at the summit of the pass from where vehicles disappear into the slopes on the Afabet side. When the leading two trucks approached the pass, the tank fired its first shot. The shell hit the side of the road and I believe that the first vehicle made it to the relative safety of the other side. The tank fired its second shot. This time the second truck was hit and started burning right at the pass itself. Eyewitnesses say that the scene looked exactly as if it were done in Hollywood.

The rest of the convoy, a rich bounty if the EPLF could capture it, got stuck all along the road leading up to the pass. EPLF fighters were quick to realize the value of the treasure in front of them and hastened to take it. It was a race that they would not win this time. The enemy was quick in his decision not to let the EPLF take the spoils. So, his troops started to use hand grenades to destroy their own weapons and vehicles. They must have found the task too difficult and dangerous. After awhile, enemy aircraft arrived at the scene and, in a few minutes, managed to turn the convoy into that fury of volcanic proportions.

As we watched the spectacle from our distance, we all exchanged words of regret that we did not come to possess that arsenal of weapons that could have made a difference in our future encounters. Only a few were salvaged. In fact, one hardy *tegadalai* dared the fire and explosion around him to pull out a truck with a Stalin's Organ on its back. On the other hand, all the burning and smoke gave us a different feeling of highly gratifying dimensions. We felt we were watching not just trucks and explosives on fire but an evil and oppressive regime burn to ashes. We consoled ourselves by regarding the spectacular colors that the explosions were forming in the sky as fireworks heralding our long-awaited victory.

We were out in the open. Heavy artillery fire from beyond Ad Sherum was falling all around us. Someone suggested that we sleep in what he thought was a relatively safe place. Ali had not been with us since morning. Adhanom too left us to climb the hills to our eastern side. These connected directly with the pass at Ad Sherum. Beghe, Hassen Sherif and myself lay side by side and tried to get some sleep. With all the persistent shelling, that was impossible.

On the morning of the 19th of March, the deadline of the contingency plan, the three of us took the same direction that Adhanom had taken the previous night. We headed for Ad Sherum. It was about 6 A.M. Beghe had his communication radio with him. He told me that, at that moment, our fighting forces were entering Afabet. When the Ad Sherum pass was blocked, our tanks had made a detour by going back to the Moga'e, turning east to the Red Sea plains and entering Afabet from that direction. The enemy had been totally defeated and routed and was being cleared out of the area.

Once on top of the hill, we stayed close to the edges overlooking the Nakfa-Afabet road and sped towards the site of final victory. The fire and smoke of the previous night had lost its initial fury, but was still substantially furious. We were close enough to feel the heat that was being carried towards us by a gentle morning breeze. The acrid smell of melting metal, plastic, tires and, yes, burning human flesh filled our nostrils. What fascinated me most was the color, shape and movement of the thick smoke down below. It was a mixture of black, gray and blue, with the yellowish-red flames visible at the core. Trapped inside the valley below the pass, it did not seem to want to rise up. It just moved, turned, started up and fell in a complex, cyclical and artistic motion. Somehow, it reminded me of the Hollywood epic, *The Ten Commandments*, where Charlton Heston divides the sea and it stands in place in an impatient state of movement.

It was a dazzling, awe-inspiring sight: like nothing I have ever seen before or since. I paused for a while to savior it, though in a dazed and—probably because of the victory—an almost drunk state of mind. Deep inside, I thanked Adhanom for having helped me be there. Ali's initial reaction would have denied me that unique opportunity. I also paid tribute to the man in the tank, who had made that historic event possible. Ad Sherum will always be remembered as the graveyard of the Ethiopian arsenal of the Nadew Front.

Before we knew it, we were within a very short distance of the pass itself. We spotted Ali's unmistakable figure. He too had seen us and beckoned us to come to him.

"So, Ali?" I asked him as we shook hands.

"*Khalas*, it's over. Our comrades have passed Afabet. They are now chasing scattered enemy troops towards Mes-halit. But, they have no way out. A whole brigade has blocked that pass."

He had a distinctive voice and manner of speaking. Even today, I could pick it out of a hundred voices. "Anything more?" we asked.

"Three Soviet officers have been taken prisoner. Besides, we now own 130 mm guns—for the first time, that is."

I stared at him almost incredulous. The most important of the Dergue's three fronts had just been broken and he had played a significant role in the realization of the whole operation. Yet he seemed to be talking about a small skirmish, about something ordinary. I suppose his calm control deterred the rest of us from jumping, shouting and hugging for joy. I was sure that, elsewhere in the base areas, there was going to be some wild celebrations the whole day and night. But, in its rightful place, right beside the melting metal below and one of the heroes of the battle with us, we all fell silent. Maybe the victory was too enormous, too significant for us to express it in any befitting way. I don't know. We just fell silent.

"Let's go down," said Ali. We went to the east of the pass. He started jumping down the rocks descending to where the Afabet plains begin. We followed him. After that day, I have traveled through the pass several times. By sheer instinct, I turn to those rocks and try to picture him jumping down to the side of the road.

"It looks like 1977 now," I said, once we had reached the bottom of the hill. "We'll be capturing towns and cities again."

"No, this time it will be different from '77. At that time all we had was the will to fight and guts. You know what our best weapons were at the time? We boasted B-10s for artillery, Browning for anti-aircraft guns and Simonovs and Kalashnikovs. Now we have both the initiative and the upper hand. We have what they call, 'a strategic advantage.'"

We talked about the victory. I told him that it was going to be very difficult for me to capture the essence and meaning of the significant event. "Do you write?" I remember asking him.

"Reports, yes. But I have never even thought of trying my hand at literature."

We talked about the importance and necessity of keeping diaries. Our conversation was too disjointed. A lot of activity was going on all around us. We kept being interrupted and distracted.

Our march towards Afabet was also disorderly. The wide expanse of land dotted by shrubs and erect boulders was full of people scattered and advancing in groups. Hundreds of civilians from Sahel who had been giving rear support during the battle were dancing and shouting as they walked or half ran along. *Tegadelti* from the various EPLF departments were also rushing towards the town as advance teams for their respective organs...and hundreds of prisoners of war were walking and limping in front of their handful of guards. Everyone sped towards Afabet.

To our right, on the western side of the plains, were some rocky hills. Stray Ethiopian soldiers were still hiding or trying to resist there. We could see some EPLF units climbing up those hills and either shooting or capturing some of them. We saw one or two surrendering without a fight. At least twice, we heard the sound of hand grenades exploding.

"Some of them are blowing themselves up rather than surrendering," Ali told us. We talked about committing suicide if totally encircled by the enemy. The history of the struggle is full of examples where *tegadelti* preferred that course than capture by the enemy. Ali said, "*Tegadalai* respects such people and applauds them. To be captured must be the worst thing that could ever happen to anyone."

Ali, Hassen Sherif and myself were walking alone, some distance to the right of the advancing multitude. Ali was worried that stray Ethiopian soldiers on the hills not far from us might cause us harm. "Cover your pistols with your shawls," he kept telling us. "Some may want to kill cadres and commanders and die. They think anyone with a pistol would have some authority."

He scanned the nearby hills as he led us. Enemy fighters and helicopters were practically moving along with us. At first, we were afraid that they might simply mow us down in those open fields. If they had, it would have been a massacre. Hundreds of people were totally exposed to such an eventuality. But the enemy now was not interested in us.

"They are searching for the arsenal and ammunition depot of this front. They don't want us to get a hold of it, so they'll want to destroy it if they can." Still, he was not sure that the pilots would not vent their frustration on us. Just as he did the first time I told him I would accompany him into the battle he repeatedly expressed his concern for Hassan's safety and mine. So he kept avoiding open spaces and took us through broken and eroded ground thick with shrubs, anthills and rocks. We passed the narrow path between Ad Sherum and Afabet and kept walking, always to the right of the main road.

It was in this area that we came across the piece of human flesh, the human heart, that I have describe in "The Heart of Tegadalai." In that essay, I try to express not only my intense feeling of the moment, but all the symbolism of the fact that a human heart could be waiting for me, lying at the gates of Afabet, as if to solve my journalistic dilemma.

At first, I doubted that the piece of flesh could actually be a human heart. We argued about this. Ali tried to clear my doubts.

"How can the heart alone be separated from the whole body? How about the muscles and whatever else that keep it firmly in place?" This was a question that many people, especially doctors and nurses, have kept asking me after they have read the article.

"It is entirely possible," answered Ali. "I've come across many such incidents."

"Have you ever come across a human heart all by itself?"

"Not necessarily the heart. But I particularly remember the day when an enemy fighter, an F-5, dropped a bomb on top of our platoon. We were all resting under a big tree and that bastard hit his target. The explosion was so powerful that many were literally thrown out of the shade. Some were half buried in the huge hole that it had dug up and we were all totally covered by thick dust, smoke and soot.

"When we recovered from the initial shock and the dust and smoke started to clear, we started to call each other. Miraculously, all except one, came out unscathed. One comrade did not move from where he lay. We examined him. At the beginning, we could not discover his wound. Then someone saw a gap on his fore-head, right at the middle. Can you believe this? When we moved his head, the skull opened and it was empty—there was no brain inside. After a long search, we found it scattered on the leaves and branches above us. Imagine," concluded Ali, "the pressure from the explosion had been so powerful that it had opened the man's skull and scattered his brain. So why can't the heart be ejected in a similar manner?"

I accepted the possibility, but kept going back to the topic, kept expressing my amazement that it could happen. He shook his head and smiled. I remember him saying, "To you, this may be something new and strange. I've seen so much that I have grown immune to the type of reaction you are showing. My life is full of gruesome memories. I choose not to remember some of it."

We fell silent for quite a while and walked on, deep in our own private thoughts. As we entered Afabet, I said to him, "Nevertheless, it is strange that a human heart should be lying at the gates of Afabet and at the moment of such a huge victory."

"You're still with it?"

"I can't get it off my mind."

"Why don't you write about it then? You can use it as a starting point to say something about the whole battle."

From that moment on, I started to compose in my mind, an essay about the heart of *tegadalai*. I felt good and inspired. Throughout the past two days, I had been searching for a way of avoiding writing a war report in my magazine. I shoved that alternative aside and did not regret having stopped to put any more notes into my diary. The heart dominated my thinking. I thanked Ali for that.

The people of Afabet were wary about pouring out into the streets to welcome us. Enemy helicopters were almost with us, far below the skies and almost close enough to lift us up by the collar. But as we passed on, the people jumped, clapped, ululated and danced within their respective compounds. Women, youths and the old alike brought water and bread and struggled to give them to us over walls and through hedges. They had to wait till the safety of the evening to go out and dance in jubilant celebration.

We were inside Afabet at about 8 A.M. the morning of the 19th. There, I met Haregot Firzun, a battalion commander and an old acquaintance. Hassen and I tried to interview him, but he refused. When I insisted, Ali told me not to pressure him too much. "Leave him for now," he said. "Don't expect fighters to talk about victory at a time like this. Remember, many comrades have not made it to this town. They have been buried between Itahalbeb and Afabet. There is a lot to mourn. You should ask him later, maybe starting from tomorrow."

I grabbed the opportunity to ask him what the human losses of his division had been. I knew he would not tell me—that just was not the EPLF's custom—but I wanted to have an idea. "I don't have the full report yet," he replied. "I am sure you are not expecting that all this victory would come for nothing. But it simply does not measure up to what I had feared it would be at the beginning."

We were very tired and wanted to take some rest. We entered a huge compound where big stores had been built. Later we learned that it had belonged to some aid organization. We found a verandah, spread our *netselas* and lay down to relax. I remember some employees of the store, young men and women, sticking their heads through half open doors to take a look at us and withdrawing quickly whenever we saw them. Our dirty, dusty clothes and unkempt hair and beards must have scared them. There was no one else in the compound to even offer us some tea. Ali slept quickly. I rarely sleep when tired. So I just lay there for hours, tired and lazy.

About 3 P.M. Ali's radio operators brought some food, water and tea, which put some life back into us. Ali then told me that he was going forward to Mes-halit, where his division had stopped after chasing its adversary. Adhanom had gone there already.

"I am going with you," I said.

"Come on, leave me alone this time!" he seemed irritated. "If it were not for Adhanom, you would not be with me today. He pushed me into allowing you to come along. We agreed that we would part here and it is here that we part. *Selamat!*"

"I want to see this process to the end. It ends at Mes-halit, doesn't it?"

"But its over, can't you see? What else is there to do? Besides, we don't even know what awaits us up front. It's a new place and we have to secure new positions. There's going to be a lot of movement up and down, nothing like the past two days. You won't enjoy it."

"That's it ?

"That's it. The whole area is also full of stray enemy soldiers. It's not going to be safe for a few days. Worse still, the enemy is going to use his air power to harass us and deter our movement. You have arrived here safe, now you go back to your place in safety. Witchu is coming in tonight. He will command this town. Go to see him. He'll tell you what to do next." He got up and, as he picked his things up, he said, "By the way, write about that heart."

As he slung his communication radio on his shoulder, he said jokingly, "Are you going to insult us again?"

"Have I ever insulted anyone?

"What else do you call all that stuff that you write in *Harbenya*?" He was referring to some articles in our magazine that had been critical of the lifestyle of some of our commanders.

"Not anymore, not in that manner, anyway," I replied smiling. "I have seen you in action. We'll make concessions...."

"Where's your wife?" he asked, changing the topic abruptly.

"In the highlands, behind enemy lines."

"When all this settles, I'll be stationed at Nakfa. If she comes to visit you, come over to see me. I'll be happy to accommodate you. But send me a message beforehand so I may make arrangements. We ought to bridge this gap between us...."

Those were his last words to me. We hugged long and tight and said goodbye. He must have been very tired. His tall and lean frame seemed to bend or stoop slightly. My eyes followed him until he disappeared from my sight.

\* \* \*

Less than a month after we had parted and within about ten days after I had written "The Heart of *Tegadalai*," I heard of Ali Ibrihim's death. Just as he had predicted, an enemy jet fighter cut him down while he, Adhanom and some others were studying ways of strengthening the new defense line at Mes-halit.

I heard about it in the evening. I sat on the edge of my bed for hours, sad and incredulous. We had been acquaintances since late 1974. The Battle for Afabet was when I was getting the chance to really know him, not just as a military commander but also as a man. I found that an even sadder coincidence. I am not qualified to talk about the gap and deprivation, in military terms, that his death created. I leave that to those who worked and fought by his side.

However, from my observations of those two or three days, I had no doubt that we had lost a sharp and able military commander. It is natural that the heart of *tegadalai* that we had both seen and about which he had urged me to write should remind me of him. It connects me to his memory. It is an image whose symbolic meaning will never be erased from my mind.

# Heart of *Tegadalai*

One hour after the capture of Afabet, my companions and I climbed down the hills of Ad Sherum to march towards that town. Jet fighters were flying very low, attempting to patrol the main road. They had such a threatening demeanor that we were forced to avoid their attention by moving as far west off the road as we could.

We were overwhelmed by the magnitude of the victory. Our internal joy was too loaded with emotion to find verbal expression. So our conversation could be nothing but disjointed. We simply kept uttering words and mumbles in dazed wonderment.

Throughout the two days of fighting, I had been with the division command that had led the attack from the heights of the Itahalbeb, Roret, the Hartetet and Ad Sherum. Therefore, I had a full picture of the course the battle had taken on the central flank. As I witnessed hills and ravines being penetrated and captured with pre-planned and amazing speed and precision, I had been a faithful chronicler. From time to time, I would take my notebook out of my pocket and jot down details I thought I should not miss—captured positions, isolated enemy units, spots of stiff enemy resistance, the challenges and cruelty of nature, the number of tanks captured…you name it, I registered with painstaking care. Since my intention was to leave an exact account to future generations, I also attempted to interpret the events of that battle as I saw them unfold in front of me.

129

As we sped through the plains of Afabet, however, I started to get the eerie feeling that I might not, after all, find the right words to suit the occasion. Where to start from, which angle or perspective to take, whom to give credit to...started to pre-occupy my mind. Our written history of the revolution is now rich with reports of decisive battles. I felt that writing another report or raving about the event in superlatives would simply not be good enough. I wanted to capture the essence, the deep source of the phenomenal fusion between planners and executors that was at the base of the fall of Afabet. The words would not come. As a writer, I started to feel inept and, as a reporter, incompetent.

Walking side by side with Ali Ibrihim, the Division Commander, I said, "And now what do we say?"

"What do you care?" he replied. "Why don't you just describe what you saw?"

"That's precisely the problem. Do I describe the victory itself or what transpired to get there. You know, the obstacles, the fatigue, the thirst... You would have done better."

"Come on," he replied. "Can't you see how we are? If at all, we may occasionally jot a few things in a diary. But to write extensively..." He did not even finish his sentence. Obviously, his attention was already focused beyond Afabet, where his troops were chasing the enemy towards Keren. I too fell silent.

Before long, however, under an indistinguishable shrub, we came across a pool of half dried blood on a flat spot dotted with scattered stones and pebbles. The flow of the blood was out of the ordinary. It had not only covered the larger part of the flat spot, but had also branched out in different directions before drying up at the edges. It had thus created a strange and awesome shape. Naturally, all three of us were attracted by the sight. At first, we thought it was a continuation of the enemy blood and corpses that we had been encountering throughout the two days. After staring at the gory sight for a while we were about to proceed when one of us pointed to a piece of flesh lying on the left edge of the drying blood. All of us bent down to examine it. It was a human heart. No bone, muscles or any other body parts, just a heart—an oily, bright and red human heart with its arteries extended towards the pool it had obviously let go. A few meters away was a tattered jacket.

"This is ours. It is the heart of a comrade," Ali Ibrihim said, almost in a whisper.

To be frank, at the beginning a cold current went down my spine and all through my body. It felt like another malaria attack. I am not the nauseous type, but this time, probably out of deference for that piece of flesh, I stepped away from it and the blood it had so strangely squeezed out. My eyes would not stop staring, even as we started to move on.

Although I restrained myself from showing it, that terribly cold flow of intense disquiet kept me shivering from head to toe. If we had not been in a hurry, I would have insisted that we bury the heart and cover the blood with earth. I was convinced that the only reason it had been left there was because, whoever had buried the rest of the body parts, had in the darkness of the previous night, simply not noticed it. We had to continue and we did. I kept glancing back at the spot until we got out of its sight.

The extreme heat and the deafening screech of the jet fighters above did not deter our rapid pace. We also resumed our discontinued, disjointed chat. But the heart refused to leave my vision. At first, I thought it was my conscience blaming me for not having buried it. Therefore, I attempted to shake it off my mind, to just forget about it. When, like a living thing, it stuck inside my mind along with its blood and arteries, however, I tried to give meaning to it. Before long it came to me with full force.

What is this cold spell, this disquiet and feeling of guilt, I asked myself. Where does this conscience come from that keeps reproaching me for not having buried that fallen heart? Its oily luster I started to see as nothing but the expression of its inherent love and goodness, and what else can its flaming redress signify but the hatred and anger it has been forced to harbor for so long? From the blood it has so generously given, will flourish the heritage and cause for which it chose to lie down there so dramatically, so defiantly.

I admonished myself for my initial feelings. A surge of pride enveloped my whole being, thus blowing away the cold shiver and disquiet, just as the winds clear the clouds to open the sky. My whole body warmed up as if a new volume of warm blood had entered my veins. Secure in the knowledge that I had finally found the very symbol that had been eluding me, I approached Afabet with a feeling of elevation. My spirit was up there in the clouds, above the whining Migs.

There was no indication of who that graceful heart had belonged to. No trace, whatsoever, of its origin, sex, religion, age, rank, or whether its owner had been a veteran or a novice. So my first reaction, naturally, was to ask who it may have been giving life to. Which direction could it have come from? Maybe with those who had rolled down steep slopes and jumped precipices to evict the enemy from the heights of the Rora; maybe with those who blitzed through the center to throw bombs at Amba, the Roret and the Hartetet; maybe, again, with those who survived the thirst of the coastal desert to attack by way of Azhara.... Try as I did, I found it impossible to give it flesh and bones and associate it with a face.

I suppose that I was simply following a simple trend of logical thinking. Soon I realized that bothering about its exact identity was just a waste of time. It was, after all, just a heart, I told myself, a heart that had extracted itself from the other organs of a human being. A heart that had refused to be buried, so it could tell its story, express its defiance and make its behest. It was simply the heart of a patriot, the heart of *tegadalai*.

I have neither the words nor the space to tell its story, explain its bravery and relay its message. Had I been a poet or a painter, I would probably have said more. I would surely never tire of eulogizing and polishing it up. Unfortunately, I am neither of these. So, since like a ring in a chain it is the link where the patriots of the past, the present and the future meet, allow me to attempt to give it its proper place and status.

In the traditions of our ancestors, the heart is the thinker, the one that mourns and rejoices, the brave, the cruel and the kind, the lover and the hater, the just and the merciless. If I were to dissect the heart of my fallen comrade, it would probably expose all of these qualities. So let me use it to reveal the secret of *tegadalai*.

Although finding it in that position is deeply moving, this is by no means the first time that this heart is shedding tears of blood for this land. I can easily stretch centuries back to relate it to those of its kind that have fallen from Halhal Bogos to Nakura, from Dogali to Gura'e, to defend the land we are fighting to liberate. But since that is a long story, let me just assert that this heart is merely following their path, simply obeying their behest.

Patriotism does not descend like manna from heaven, nor can it be created from naught by a magic wand. Our fallen heart has its origins in history, in the ancestral legends and traditions that have come to us through generations. This land of ours has never seen, nor has it enjoyed for ages, the benefits of normal peace and ordinary life. Centuries of foreign rule, invasions and internal strife have seen to it that our people do not breathe the air of peace and tranquility. Consequently, the love of country that the *tegadalai* has inherited is not merely one of ordinary love and compassion. Hate and defiance claim an equal share in his or her passions and emotions. History has pushed the *tegadalai* to be quick and ferocious in retaliation to any threat, any provocation that endangers Eritrea's rights.

No wonder that I saw that morning kindness and anger at the same time, two opposites in the same heart. And had I been witnessing both phenomena! Who could ever count the enemy corpses lying at every turn, every ravine and every hill in the most grotesque of postures. Who could tally the captured tanks and burnt out weaponry? Would I be accused of mystification if I were to declare that this heart actually spits fire to burn metal and that it is destined for loftier deeds? When I witnessed it cross the thirsty plains, climb the Hartetet which had almost killed me in the relative leisure after battle, capture that summit and go on to fight at Ad Sherum without so much as a respite, even I envied its perseverance. And when I noticed the terror of its venom in the eyes of newly captured enemy soldiers, I swear that, although my own side and my own shelter, I too trembled with awe.

If I had seen anger and terror alone, I would have had cause to worry. I would have paused to wonder whether life in the wilderness had not extracted every bit of compassion from the heart of *tegadalai*. Once in Afabet, however, I noted with relief that beneath all that battlefield cruelty lay an inherent softness, a sea of compassion. Its handling of Ethiopian prisoners of war is too well known for me to dwell on here. One would expect, though, that its reaction to the three captured Soviet officers would be different. It was not. These were part of the system that had helped drive the Eritrean revolution from the fringes of Asmara to the foxholes of Sahel. These were the very officers whose bombs had rained on trenches and villages, on fighters and unarmed civilians with indiscriminate fury. And yet, the *tegadelti* that I saw flocking around them were there just to see what they looked like. I saw no hostility in them, neither was there any verbal abuse.

Theirs is not a heart of grudges and evil intentions. Afabet convinced me that this is a heart of mercy and forgiveness—a heart, indeed, that does not spend sleepless nights in gnawing plots of hate and vengeance. Obviously, it does not want to see repeated, even on its enemies, the pain and ordeal it has had to suffer. Nor would it covet from others what is not rightfully its due. The world has yet to recognize this heart that so willingly sheds all that it possesses for peace among men and women. As to the powerful of our age who are intent on crushing it for the success of their own global strategies, I say that they do not understand its nature. Or, possibly, they are deluding themselves.

For this is a heart that is capturing their weapons and even men with their own weapons. Indeed, it is a heart that has raised its head to defy their awesome power for one quarter of a century. And like the piece of flesh and the symbol of courage that we found resisting the scourge of the morning sun, it will not be long before the mighty accept that the heart of *tegadalai* is not about to disintegrate or to burst out of existence even when trampled on. That they have not done so till now, that they are not pausing to listen to its beat, is a waste.

It is a big one then, this heart of *tegadalai*; and because adversity, fortitude and the flames of war have fomented it into maturity, it has reached a new height. However it will need careful handling especially in this, its moments of victory, lest it get intoxicated with glory, forget what it has gone through, swell out of proportion and just blow up. True, the fact that the people of Afabet could welcome it safe from any harm to their person or property is relieving and encouraging. It is also an indication of its future relations with its people.

Nevertheless, a heart without a guide may prove fickle and flighty and we will need to cultivate, expand, educate and make it wise. A product of the people, it was nurtured by the people. In return, it has shed tears of blood for them. It has fallen for their sake. It is, therefore, incumbent upon this heart to tune its beat with theirs, to preserve their culture and protect their honor, to understand their problems and seek solutions for them. It has the obligation to approach them, not from an attitude of superiority and disdain but with modesty and humbleness. Above all, we have the duty to guarantee that it renews its oath and lives up to it's responsibility never to assume the role of dispenser of freedom and never to ride over its own people.

Sitting on the rocks above what was the Ethiopian "Nadew Command," I let my eyes wander over Afabet. It has definitely expanded and developed. There is no doubt that the enemy had meant to settle for good. I sent my memory back almost ten years to when we had withdrawn to the mountains of Sahel. At that time, we had not retreated by ourselves. We had been accompanied by the dozens of tanks and the thousands of prisoners of war that we had captured at those historical battles of Elabered and Ma'imide.

It was a cruel and testing time, but we had emerged from it richer and stronger. A lot has transpired since—we pushed and were pushed, we attacked and were raided, we inflicted heavy damages but, in truth, we also paid dearly. We buried our heroes. From a distance, I could see strategic weapons being pulled into town. From the B-10s of ten years ago to the B-24 "Stalin organs" is a big jump. Where to now? Keren or Asmara? Or, as a remote possibility, maybe back to our impregnable trenches up around Nakfa?

As an individual who has known and participated in this Front from its relative childhood, and who has seen it overcome misfortune and emerge from bottle necks, I trust that, forging forward or turning back will not make much difference. Either way will make us sturdier and bring us ever nearer to final victory. I am not worrying and for no other reason than the fact that our direction reassures me—because I have seen and have come to believe.

Above all, though, I have a behest to uphold. A behest made by that charming and purple heart of *tegadalai*, which I found lying at the gates of Afabet, as if to represent all the martyrs who had fallen from Sidoha Eila to Gheregir Sudan, from Semhar to Barka, on the front lines or in the base areas, in towns or in the countryside, for the very land that it had so bloodied.

From the EPLF magazine *Harbenya*, No 7, May 1988

# PLAYS

## Life in the Camp of the Enemey

# Le'ul

## A One-Act Play in Five Scenes

### Scene One

*In a small part of a textile factory, three women workers are wrapping up their daily chores. It is a routine job, involving folding and packing bundles of finished products. They are so accustomed to the drudgery of the assembly line that they seem to work without thinking. What pleasure they may have found in their work is definitely gone. The atmosphere is thus one of a strange mix of nonchalance and boredom, but also of efficiency....*

*To the extreme left of the audience is Le'ul, busy folding or rolling what appears to be a bundle of khaki cloth. She is tall and gives the impression of dignified composure. She also seems pre-occupied with something else, there is sadness in her eyes. A second woman, Kidisti, is at center stage. She is active, maybe excessively so. Much older that her companion, she is nevertheless impressively quick and agile. A third woman, Letegergish, is the youngest. Her hairdo, which she touches and straightens between chores, is fashionable. She is, obviously, not interested in her work and pays little attention to what her companions are saying. Kidisti is worried about Le'ul. After stealing two or three glances at her, she starts to talk.*

139

**Kidisti:** You are mourning too much, Le'ul....You look so sickly. People can hardly recognize you. Come, talk to me, make me feel at ease.

**Le'ul:** I have overcome that, my dear Kidisti, I am not mourning any more. And there is nothing I can do about it. But, this endless work is not giving us time to breathe. Toiling and bending day in and day out....

**Kidisti:** Bending, yes, bending is the right word. Fifteen years, today is my fifteenth year in this work, in this room. Are you listening to me?

**Le'ul:** I am listening. You have been repeating this the whole day. You know, it means that you started working when we were little children.

**Kidisti:** Of course, in the Haile Selassie years, when Asrate Kassa was the governor here, I used to earn one Birr and ten cents a day at the time...but let me tell you, I used to buy more with that meager amount than what I buy with the 1.90 Birr they throw at us today. Sweat and backaches through winter and summer and what do we get? Fines, deductions, no food on the plates, hungry children....This is no life, Le'ul.

**Le'ul:** Don't be so upset, my sister. Problems don't stay forever. Remember? They go as they come. Just keep everything inside you. Be patient.

**Kidisti:** You are the one who knows how to be patient, Le'ul. The Virgin May awarded you quintals of it. Me? Me...I just can't relax unless I breathe out what agitates my poor heart.

140

*As Le'ul and Kidisti speak, Letegergish is seen removing her complazione or gown and straightening up her dress. She fishes a hand mirror from her bag, comes towards the audience to the fore of the stage and starts making herself up.*

**Letegergish:**   Isn't it time to go yet?

**Kidisti:**   Ah, lucky Letegergish, you can't wait for the time to go. Do you know what the sound of the bell means to us? Home and children with little to eat. It is a soul-wrenching feeling.

**Letegergish:**   *(totally unmoved and speaking into her mirror.)* So, what am I supposed to do about that? It is not my fault that you have piles of children.

**Kidisti:**   *(derisively.)* Oh no, Sofia, please don't say that.

*Letegergish winces when called 'Sofia' and is visibly angry, but she pretends not to have heard. Le'ul notices this.*

**Le'ul:**   *Mbwa*, why are you calling her 'Sofia?'

**Kidisti:**   It is not I who calls her that. You know Kelemu, that ugly technician? At the gate this morning, I heard him call her, 'Sofia,' *(in fake imitation.)* and she answers, 'Woy, Kelly....'

**Letegergish:**   *(swinging back in fury.)* Woman, watch out for your own dignity. I will do to my name what I want. If it pleases me I can switch from Sofia to Helen and back again. You are just a jealous old woman whom no one notices anymore.

**Kidisti:**   *(arms akimbo.)* You cheap, insolent girl. How dare you say that to me, a respectable, married woman ....

141

**Le'ul:** Women, please control your selves. We have enough problems as it is, we don't need your constant bickering. Letegergish, you are younger, please calm down.

**Letegergish:** You calm her down, first. She calls me cheap? Just because I respect her for her age...she's sitting on my head.

**Kidisti:** You're disgraceful!

**Letegergish:** Disgraceful, yourself! *(At this moment, the Cadre enters the stage from one of the inside doors. She is tall and proud. She is not involved in manual work, hence, she is well-dressed. Letegergish is first to see her. She straightens up quickly and moves towards her.)* Good afternoon, my Cadre.

**Cadre:** *(measures up Le'ul and Kidisti with her eyes.)* Every time I come into this room, you are either quarreling or gossiping. Why is that so?

**Le'ul:** Because we just finished our portion for the day. But at other times....

**Cadre:** Who asked you? *(turning to Letegergish.)* Why?

**Letegergish:** Matters keep coming up.

**Cadre:** And what came up this time?

**Letegergish:** *(pointing at Kidistt.)* She attacked me for having greeted Kelemu this morning and I was telling her it was none of her business.

**Cadre:** *(to Kidisti.)* Does it bother you, if she greets Kelemu?

142

**Kidisti:** Oh no, my Cadre, it does not bother me at all. As far as I am concerned, she can go right ahead and greet the whole of Asmara.

**Cadre:** Who gives you the right to wiggle you tongue any direction you want? Besides, is it your responsibility to tell her whom to greet and when? Or, *(giving Le'ul a meaningful glare.)* are there people in this company who secretly cause havoc and disruption so there may not be peace amongst you, so you may fight each other? There must be some who tell you whom to greet and whom to just pass.

*Kidisti does not reply, but gives Letegergish a steady and angry stare. Backstage, the ring or chiming of a bell is heard and it is time to go. Here, there is a flutter of movement from all three of them. Letegergish, bag in hand, starts towards the exit; Le'ul and Kididti also move to pick up their respective netselas....*

**Cadre:** *(in a steady, commanding voice.)* You have not been dismissed yet. Letegergish, wait for me outside, I have something to tell you. *(Letegergish exits. The Cadre addresses Kidisti.)* I have just decided that you be fined for your loose tongue.

**Kidisti:** *(dismayed, but asking, not begging.)* You can pass me this time, my Cadre. At least, for the sake of my children. Last week, half of my daily pay was cut off just because I broke a needle...and now, again....

**Cadre:** No more talk, just leave!

**Kidisti:** *(throwing her netsela around her shoulder and exiting.)* So be it, the Virgin Mary is up there....

*The Cadre and Le'ul are now confronting each other across the stage — they are almost on the two extreme sides of the room. The cadre is try-*

143

*ing to intimidate Le'ul by sizing her up with her eyes and maintain-*
*ing a heavy silence for some seconds. Le'ul, composed as usual, waits for*
*an obvious showdown. The atmosphere is tense.*

**Cadre:** Hmm! What does the directive on our green revolution campaign tell us to do?

**Le'ul:** *(as if by rote.)* That every worker must produce three
times more than he or she was producing before the
campaign was launched.

**Cadre:** If that is so, then why did I find you just now, during working hours, with your arms folded?

**Le'ul:** Today, because I had finished my part. But at other
times, I don't remember ever folding my arms in
time of work.

**Cadre:** You are quite adept at giving short replies, aren't
you? But, when it comes to gossip, your tongue
stretches quite a distance.

**Le'ul:** *Mbwa!*

**Cadre:** Yes, you have been reported as having said that your
rights had been denied you.

**Le'ul:** *(taken aback a little, but controlling her surprise as*
*quickly.)* I did not say that my rights had been
denied me. In my sorrow and anger, though, I did
say to someone, 'What harm would it do them if
they gave me a two-or three-day leave?' Those were
my exact words.

**Cadre:** 'We have been denied our rights,' those were your
exact words. Stop fooling yourself, we hear every
thing. Even the walls tell us what you say. But, I have

144

|          |                                                                                     |
|----------|-------------------------------------------------------------------------------------|
|          | a question. You said you were sad and angry. Why? Aren't you well protected and provided for by our revolutionary government? |
| Le'ul:   | A week ago, I lost and buried my first and only child. I asked that I be allowed a three-day leave so I may receive my visitors; I was denied that. That is why I am still sad and angry. |

**Cadre:** If we allow three-day leaves to every woman who loses a baby, do you think that our production targets will be met?

**Le'ul:** *(in a low, but bitter voice.)* I was only thinking about my child.

**Cadre:** *(raises her voice in irritation.)* This is one more proof of your anti-production attitude. Three days! We are not asking you not to mourn your child. We are not cruel. But you must swallow your sorrow, keep it within you. Our directive tells us to gear all our attention and energy towards the success of the production campaign. That is what we should do. Besides, you are a young and strong woman, you can have other babies. Why mourn so much?

**Le'ul:** *(Unable to control her emotions anymore, Le'ul explodes in anger. She moves half way towards the Cadre and looks her straight in the eyes.)* What did you say? I am a mother! For nine months that child was here, in my womb. I was making ends meet just to raise him. He died in my arms because I did not have the money the doctors asked me to pay. And you stand here to tell me that I can have other babies? What guarantee to longer life do the unborn have in our situation?

**Cadre:** *(tilts and slowly shakes her head as if gravely disap-*

*pointed at Le'ul's words.)* Aha, so this is your answer. I know that you have no trust or confidence in our revolution. We shall see about that.

*The Cadre exits. Le'ul sits abruptly on a nearby stool and stares at the floor—pensive but also agitated. Mussie, a worker, enters.*

**Mussie:** Le'ul!

**Le'ul:** *(startled by his voice.)* Mussie, you scared me.

**Mussie:** Are you crazy? What are you doing here, all alone? Get up and go home before they accuse you of something. Here, take your *netsela*.

**Le'ul:** We are surrounded by squealers, Mussie. Are we going to survive this? I don't know who told on me, but the Cadre was just accusing me of having said that we had been denied our rights.

**Mussie:** I know, it was probably Letegergish. I saw them outside. They were whispering and pointing. I had asked you to be careful with her. But, leave that to me. Now, please hurry, go home.

**Le'ul:** What home, Mussie? Even home has become a place of turmoil. Why don't you come there and talk to your friend for his own sake and mine? He always listens to you.

**Mussie:** He just buried his son. What could he possibly be doing that would upset you so?

**Le'ul:** I am more than upset, I dread that house, Mussie. Your friend is drinking every day. Even in this period of mourning, he did not come home last night. Fear at work, sorrow and torment at home....I am

146

feeling cluttered, I am being cornered. I can't be of any use here anymore. Make contacts, Mussie, please send me away.

**Mussie:** No-no-no-no. And who will run things here? Who will stand up for the cause? Do you want this city to be dominated by liars and cadres? You want Letegergish and her like to do as they please? Look at poor souls like Kidisti. Who will they have to lean on? I will come to your place and talk to my friend Weldu myself. You know Weldu, he just goes into these seasonal sprees and then comes back to his senses. Come, come....We don't want to be discovered here alone.... *(moving out.)* That will mean a lot of trouble....

**Le'ul:** *(Resigned to his advice, she spreads her netsela and rises.)* As you wish...let's go. *(They exit.)*

## Scene Two

*Weldu and Le'ul's house. A medium-sized room—about 4x5 meters. It is modestly furnished—a* fernello *in the background, a double-bed to the extreme left, a second-hand cup-board to the right, a table with three chairs in the middle—a typical Asmara working-class home. Everything is neatly arranged, the bed sheets spotless clean...etc.*

*Le'ul, sad and pensive, is putting away her dead son's baby clothes and diapers into an old box pulled out from underneath the bed. After a few seconds, Weldu comes in through the entrance, situated near the cupboard to the right of the audience. Without uttering a word, he pulls a chair and slumps on it, tired and careless. Le'ul too does not speak to him. She spreads one injera on a large plate, and pours some shiro in the middle of it. She places the food on the table in front of Weldu and goes back to folding the clothes. The silence between them is heavy. Weldu takes two or three bites, but pushes the food away from him.*

**Le'ul:**    Aren't you going to eat?

**Weldu:**    I've had enough...I'm full. *(He gives the room a blank stare—looks at the ceiling, the floor, their whole property, and speaks almost to himself.)* I hate this house. I don't even know if it is because it reminds me of my son or because I simply don't like it anymore.

**Le'ul:**    *(also almost to herself.)* Your feeling for this house is not something new.

**Weldu:**    *(He does not seem to have heard her.)* What? *(Le'ul gives no response. But now he talks to her.)* Listen, I have no money this month, I'm broke. We should start looking for some way out.

**Le'ul:**    What now? How about your salary?

**Weldu:** Last month, when I was working on an engine, I broke a chain. They sliced off half of my wages.

**Le'ul:** Again?

**Weldu:** What am I to them?

**Le'ul:** And what happened to the rest?

**Weldu:** The rest...well, I had debts to settle and it is gone.

**Le'ul:** Very well, we go empty stomach this month. What do you expect my meager salary to settle? House rent? Electricity? Food?

**Weldu:** Oho, don't forget your mother. You do send things to her, you know?

**Le'ul:** You make an issue of the handful of coffee beans I send her once in a while? I never ask you to account for the debts you say you settle. I don't even know what those debts are.

**Weldu:** (*raising his voice.*) So, why don't you ask for an account? Come, ask for an account. While we are at it, ask me also me where I was last night. I am waiting.

**Le'ul:** Please, Weldu, let us not fight. For the sake of our marriage, for the sake of the child we just buried, please, let me be.

**Weldu:** (*striking the table in anger.*) Let you be? You are asking me to let you be? Am I the one who is picking fights? Don't I too care for our marriage? It's just...its the money...it just isn't enough.

**Le'ul:** (*leaning on the table to get closer to him.*) What money

149

is not enough, Weldu? Do you realize what you are saying? Ever since you started going around and drinking with those people, what have you done for this house. They are not even worth your company. How many things do you think you can do with your 180 Birr? Then you tell me to ask you where you were last night? I know where you spend your evenings and nights, Weldu. I am just waiting patiently for you to come back.

**Weldu:** *(Weldu stands from his chair in rage.)* Enough! I've heard enough. You dare to talk to me like that! Those cadres at the factory must be teaching you new words and manners.

**Le'ul:** *(in rare and uncharacteristic fury.)* Cadres? I don't learn words and manners from trash, from those scum! You are my husband, Weldu. It is only because it is my duty to respect you that I am being so patient with you. My friends are talking about us. They are calling me a drunkard's wife and they are calling you a drifter. You think I enjoy that? Workers like you are performing miracles, but look at you ....

**Weldu:** Who do you think you're talking to? *(He slaps her on the left cheek with the back of his right hand. The force of the strike causes her head to jerk. She stops talking and bows her head.)* We'll see about drinking and drifting.

*Weldu moves towards the door, but pauses in front of the audience. He takes a handkerchief out of his pocket and wipes the perspiration on his forehead. He then exits quickly. Le'ul still stands on the spot she was slapped by Weldu. After he is gone, she starts touching her cheek. She is also weeping. Slowly, she starts to clean the table. In a short while, there is a knock on the door, but it opens since Weldu had left it half-closed. Mussie walks in.*

| | |
|---|---|
| **Mussie:** | Hey, Le'ul, Weldu! Are you people home? Have you stopped locking your door? *(He sees Le'ul and stops as he notices her crying.)* |
| **Le'ul:** | Mussie? |
| **Mussie:** | You're still weeping? Is it the baby? Aren't you stretching this mourning a bit too far. |
| **Le'ul:** | *(wiping her tears and trying to compose herself.)* It is not the baby this time. I am overcoming that. Mourning the dead devastates you only while it lasts...but it fades away. What is impossible to bear is mourning the living. It crushes you every day. |
| **Mussie:** | Aren't you overreacting? What is it? Have you quarreled again? There's a bruise on your cheek, he must have struck you. |
| **Le'ul:** | Weldu is leading an aimless and unproductive life here. I would have much preferred to have seen him go away with his friends. He is neither here nor there. Look at me, I can't even pay my monthly contributions anymore. Send me to the field, Mussie. I am just no use here. |
| **Mussie:** | Don't keep repeating this request. You are not going. The field is not a hiding place; it is not a haven from personal problems. The question right now is how to make Weldu become his old self. Why are you becoming so jumpy? Brace yourself. *(rises from the chair.)* I think I know where he is. I'll go and try to put some sense into his head. Whichever way, we will find a solution. If he persists on this same route, then we will look for other ways. I need to see you tomorrow at noon. There's some work. *(starts to leave.)* |
| **Le'ul:** | Wait, eat something. I have some sugar, I'll make you tea. |

**Mussie:**   No, no, I'm not hungry. I'll make him come back here before the curfew.

**Le'ul:**   Ok, ciao.

## Scene Three

*A small bar. Weldu is sitting alone drinking ouzo or anice. The only other person is a woman bartender. Amharic music is blaring from a radio.*

**Weldu:**   Pour some more.

**Bartender:**   *(brings a half full bottle of ouzo and stands playfully in front of him.)* This is your fourth round.

**Weldu:**   What if it is my tenth? What of it?

**Bartender:**   Well, I mean, you're drinking alone.

**Weldu:**   Has drinking alone also been forbidden?

**Bartender:**   *(pouring ouzo into a mini glass.)* No...but in the good old days people used to talk to us and invite us to drink with them. But, nowadays, everyone just comes, drinks alone and goes away. *(She pulls a chair and moves to sit beside Weldu.)*

**Weldu:**   *(dismissing her with a wave of the hand.)* Please go and change the music.

**Bartender:**   *(pouting at him and picking up the bottle.)* It's listener's choice honey, from Radio Ethiopia—it is my favorite program and I won't change it.
   *(As the bartender walks towards her counter, Mussie walks in and approaches her. Weldu has his back towards Mussie.)*

| | |
|---|---|
| **Mussie:** | *(in a low voice so Weldu won't hear.)* Has he been here long? |
| **Bartender:** | About half an hour. |
| **Mussie:** | Is he drunk? |
| **Bartender:** | Not really, but he'll get there at the rate he is drinking.<br>*(Mussie pulls a chair and sits by Weldu. The latter sees him for the first time and lowers his head, somewhat embarrassed.)* |
| **Mussie:** | Selam. Weldu. |
| **Weldu:** | *Salve*, Mussie. What will you have? Hey, *barrista*, bring that bottle. |
| **Mussie:** | No, no, I am not drinking. *(The bartender brings the bottle to the table, but Mussie prevents her from serving him. In the meantime, Weldu has downed his fourth glass. The bartender pours him a fifth.)* I passed by your house. Le'ul told me you had just left. So I came after you. How have you been? |
| **Weldu:** | How do you expect me to have been? Same as you saw me the last time. Even worse. And then? The same as I had been the previous time. All we see is things getting worse and worse, no improvement. At work, they are deducting our pay even for faults we never committed. Our children die in our arms for lack of care, treatment money. And home? Oh, home...*(imitating Le'ul.)* 'Where were you? Where did you spend last night?' This is a dog's life, *e una vita canaglia*! *(He picks the glass to drink up, but Mussie takes it into his grip and pushes it away from Weldu. Weldu stretches to reach out for it and is irri-* |

153

*tated by Mussie's action.)*

**Mussie:** *Vita canaglia?* Is this a solution for a dog's life?

**Weldu:** Come on, Mussie, sometimes you sound like these *Pente* or *Coste*...whatever you call them. What friend do I have except *ouzo?* Those days are gone, Mussie, when you-know-who were here. Great and happy days. But, they left us. So what do we do? We drink so we may forget them, and we drink so we may not remember ourselves.

**Mussie:** But why do you want to forget yourself?

**Weldu:** And why should I remember it? What purpose will that serve? What would I do for it? Even my soul is so deep in debt, I don't consider it mine anymore. My rights, the law...all keep passing me by. And our dear friends preach revolution to us. I'm just a servant, Mussie, a slave.... *(stretches his hand towards his glass.)*

**Mussie:** *(holds the glass firmly in his grip. As he speaks, he glances at the bartender to check if she had heard Weldu.)* Sh...sh...Do you realize where you are and what you are saying? You roam the bars and expose yourself like this? Don't you understand that these are times when you should not trust your own shadow?

**Weldu:** *Ma dai lasci stare....(sends his hand to the glass.)*

**Mussie:** *Ma dai dai (snatches the glass away and spills its contents on the floor. He goes towards the bartender to pay. Weldu is annoyed and at a loss as to what to do next.)* How much?

**Bartender:** Two Birr fifty. *(Mussie pays her.)*

**Mussie:** *(returns to Weldu.)* Let's go now, I have things to say to you. We still have an hour before curfew. Come, we have to hurry to our homes.

**Weldu:** *(still sitting.)* I don't have a home. I've been kicked out, she kicked me out.

**Mussie:** Just come, will you? *(He holds Weldu by the arm and helps him rise and they start walking towards the entrance, on the right foreground of the stage. The bartender is seen cleaning the table.)* I wish we all had a home like yours, Weldu. It is strange how you wander around aimlessly with a woman like Le'ul in the house. Remember how you used to bore us with endless talk about her and how many times you said you loved her?

**Weldu:** *(in a subdued voice.)* I still love her. It's the money that's making us fight. It just is not enough.

*They linger at the entrance to the bar and Mussie talks to Weldu in a low voice. The audience cannot hear what is being said. Clearly, Mussie is giving Weldu a lot of advice and Weldu is listening intently, sometimes looking at the sky, sometimes nodding or scratching his head.. They exit.*

## Scene Four

*Back in Weldu and Le'ul's home. It is late evening and Le'ul is preparing to sleep. Weldu is not in yet.*

**Le'ul:**     *(to herself) Oromai*, Le'ul Seyoum. From now onwards, just get used to the idea of sleeping by yourself. Aye, Weldu...all that love, and now? I could have been a little more patient tonight. Maybe he would have stayed.

*As she unbuttons her dress or shirt, the sound of keys turning is heard. Sitting on the bed, Le'ul turns to the door expectantly. Weldu comes in. His earlier intoxication appears gone. For a few seconds, he stands in the middle of the room and they stare at each other. Weldu pulls a chair and sits. Le'ul continues to sit for a while. Careful not to give away her earlier feelings of regret, she rises with deliberate reluctance and approaches him with a serious face. When she speaks, she sounds hurt, which she actually is.*

**Le'ul:**     It is the same food, but would you like to eat something?

**Weldu:**     Like the foolish shepherd who declined lunch only to beg for supper? All right, I'll eat. *(Le'ul smiles grudgingly and brings the same plate and food. She moves to go back to her bed.)* Aren't you eating with me? Please....

*Obviously, Weldu is ashamed of what he had done and is prepared to make amends. Le'ul pulls a chair hesitantly, slices off a bit of injera and begins to nibble at it. The silence between them is discomfiting. Weldu cannot bear it and he fidgets as he steals glances at Le'ul.*

**Weldu:**     Why don't you eat?

**Le'ul:**     I'm eating. *(more silence.)*

| | |
|---|---|
| **Weldu:** | *(giving her a playful nudge with his elbow.)* Come on, eat. *(Weldu is so comical that Le'ul cannot contain her laughter and she utters some words of protest as she pushes his elbow back. Weldu too sounds a short, shy laughter. But, silence reigns once again.)* By the way, I met Mussie this evening. |
| **Le'ul:** | I know, he went from here, looking for you. *(Silence.)* |
| **Weldu:** | We talked a lot. |
| **Le'ul:** | That's fine. *(Another long silence.)* |
| **Weldu:** | *(Unable to bear the whole mood anymore, he throws back the roll of injera he was about to swallow. He turns to her and looking her straight in the eyes, he starts talking.)* Listen Le'ul, I was angry this afternoon. I didn't mean to hit you, much less hurt you. I see your face bruised and I can't believe I did this. I just was not myself...I am not myself anymore. My friends have gone, I am living below my peers and likes...I'm saying and doing things that are strange even to me...I don't know what else to say. |
| **Le'ul:** | All right, I can let things go this time. What is past is past. But from now onwards... |
| **Weldu:** | From now onwards? God is my witness, I will never even remove a fly from your face without your permission. This happened in a fit of anger, I can't even recall how it happened. I've done you wrong, Le'ul, there is no denying it. |
| **Le'ul:** | *(volunteering to make him feel a little better by easing his remorse.)* Maybe my words were also a little too harsh. Maybe I shouldn't have said some of the things I did. |

**Weldu:** *(grabbing the opportunity.)* Yes, exactly. Come to think of it, you did provoke me, you know. Otherwise, you know me, I'm not a violent person, am I? Would you call me violent?

**Le'ul:** *(smiling teasingly.)* Oh no, I wouldn't.

**Weldu:** *(With the tension dissipated, he starts to feel at ease and eats heartily.)* Mussie explained a lot of things to me. Half of it I understood, the rest just went over my head. I don't even know where he got all those words from....'You are fighting against your own interests,' he says to me, and then he goes on and says, 'Be, careful, they are going to destroy you....' He just went on clobbering me.

**Le'ul:** He is your friend. He knows you well. Who else can say that to you?

**Weldu:** But it's his words I am amazed about. Some of them are difficult to understand. Even you use the same language sometimes...'interests,' 'struggle'...I don't even know how you came to know them. In fact, I don't know much of anything anymore. Am I changing? I know I've always been a bit hot-tempered, even small matters make me angry. Maybe nowadays I am aroused more quickly than ever before. I admit that. But, then, it used to be that my flares would last five minutes, *cinque minuti e basta.* Oh God, I get angry every minute and stay angry the whole day.

**Le'ul:** It is the times we live in, Weldu. These are not easy days. Let alone you and your temper, even I find myself upset and complaining. Remember our honeymoon? Your friends used to call me 'Le'ul the Silent.'

158

| | |
|---|---|
| **Weldu:** | Maybe it's their meetings, these 'enlightenment' seminars that are tearing us all apart. We should rename them, 'seminars on disharmony or disorder.' How I'd love to see their own bowels disordered. *(Le'ul starts to laugh.)* I'm telling you, I'm serious. I mean people are not focused anymore. Go to the streets and you won't find a single happy face. Frowns, all sorts of spots on every feature....Even the beautiful have turned ugly. |
| **Le'ul:** | *(pushing the food towards him.)* Eat while you talk. |
| **Weldu:** | *(picks a roll, but throws it back on the plate to make a point.)* I almost forgot. Yesterday our new manager called a meeting and I tell you these people are simply shameless. He stands in front of us and says, 'The people of Asmara have been smiling happily for quite sometime now. This is because they are relaxed and content deep inside....' I was so amazed, I just said, 'Sir, do you have a slice of conscience at all?' |
| **Le'ul:** | *(Startled by what he said, she cowers.)* You said that at the meeting? |
| **Weldu:** | I did too, just blurted it out...in my heart. |
| **Le'ul:** | *(relieved and laughing.)* Ufff...that's better. |
| **Weldu:** | Hey, you think I'm crazy? I wouldn't say that in front of these barbarians. I don't want you to run to the Expo every morning—to feed me. |
| **Le'ul:** | *(feeling nostalgic or romantic.)* It all sounds just like the old times again. |
| **Weldu:** | I am trying to bring the old times back, Le'ul. I've been blind and foolish too long. |

**Le'ul:**  I'm glad you say that; that's what I want too. We both break our backs in our thankless jobs. We should find consolation at home. We ought to support and encourage each other. Our quarrels merely serve those who are strangling our throats and sucking our blood. *(Weldu stares at her open-mouthed, obviously impressed by her words. He is about to say something, but she interrupts him.)* Hey, hey, this conversation is getting longer and its quite late now. Let's go to bed.

**Weldu:**  Yes, let's do that. We don't want to oversleep in the morning and go in late. That's half a day's pay gone...that'll mean no money for house rent, no coffee for Mamma.... *(He puts his arms around her shoulders and she hugs him too. They laugh and go towards their bed. They do not even clean the table.)*

## Scene Five

*The factory a few days later. Le'ul's face is much brighter and happier. Kidisti is busy with her work. Letegergish is not in the room.*

**Le'ul:** *(pointing to Letegergish's place.)* Where did that one go?

**Kidisti:** I don't know. She dashed out suddenly. Maybe she went to squeal, that treacherous rat!

**Le'ul:** She won't catch us unawares from now onwards. You also stop talking in front of her.

**Kidisti:** *Wai*, I will not even notice her. *(pauses to assess Le'ul for a moment.)* You know your face has lit up once more these past few days. That cloud of sadness, poor Le'ul, I am glad it is gone. *(Le'ul smiles and shakes her head, ever wondering at Kidisti's openness of heart.)* By the way, my sister Alganesh wrote to me from Italy.

**Le'ul:** Oh, congratulations.

**Kidisti:** Yes, she wrote. She says to me, 'How are you? How is every kith and kin?' And then she said something I did not quite understand. She said that she's working with some people, on something sounding mysterious. She also used a strange word, something like *'tewedibe'* or *'tedawibe'*. My neighbor's daughter was reading the letter for me, so I just took it away from her. You never know with children, they talk too much. Do you know what *'tewedibe'* means?

**Le'ul:** *(pretending to think hard.)* It might mean registered into an association.

**Kidisti:** *(stops what she is doing abruptly.)* What? Associations in Italy too? Like these associations?

161

**Le'ul:** *(indicating a far away place with her head.)* Not these associations...the others...you know....

**Kidisti:** *(raises her eyebrows.)* Aha! Those associations....How stupid of me not to guess. Le'ul, do you know how to be one of them? I would register, you know.

**Le'ul:** No, I don't know anything about that, my sister. *(The Cadre enters from a door in the background. Letegergish is behind her. Le'ul and Kidisti stop talking and busy themselves.)*

**Cadre:** So, are you gossiping as usual?

**Le'ul:** *(coldly.)* We are not.

**Kidisti:** Actually we are hurrying to finish before the bell rings.

**Cadre:** *(derisively.)* How come then your expressions say something else, emm? Anyway, let me get to my point. The woman who was your *maestra* before has been transferred to another branch. She is being replaced by Letegergish, who is to be your *maestra* from now on. Until we bring a replacement for Lete, you'll have to double your efforts and cover her daily portions. *(She notices that Kididsti is unhappy with the announcement.)* Yes, Kidisti, you seem surprised.

**Kidisti:** Oh no, it's been a long time since I cured myself of that. No more surprises for me, my Cadre.

**Cadre:** Good, a similar good fortune awaits both of you provided you are diligent and revolutionary enough. You are being directed to obey her and follow her example. *(to Kidisti.)* But you better shorten your tongue, it is a bit too long. *(to Letegergish.)* And it is your responsibility to supervise them and make them work properly. *(She slowly turns towards Le'ul and once again they are eye-to-eye.)* As for you.... *(She just gives Le'ul a threatening nod and exits.)*

*Le'ul and Kidisti stand upright and give Letergergish such a steady stare that she is at a loss as to what to do. Embarrassed, she makes some unnecessary movements—lifts and drops things...etc. At last, unable to stand the atmosphere, she picks up her purse and sweater and prepares to leave.*

**Letegergish:** It is about time to go. So, place everything in order, clean-up and go. *(moves to exit.)*

**Kidisti:** *(places her hands behind her back and makes an elaborate bow.)* But yes, *maestra*, immediately.

**Letegergish:** *(turns back and faces her.)* No need for you to bow. That backward custom is no longer necessary and you know it. Don't ridicule me.

**Kidisti:** *(ridiculing her.)* Oh no, ridiculing is not part of me, my sister. My whole house, the whole clan forbids mocking people. I did it only because we were just told to respect you.

**Letegergish:** Does that mean you should bow to me?

**Kidisti:** Well, no. But, don't threaten, my daughter. I thought I was doing the right thing...just to be like you, to be called 'a revolutionary', maybe even to become a *maestra*. I had no ill-intentions.

**Letegergish** *(gets angry.)* Are you implying that I became a *maestra* by bowing?

**Kidisti:** Wait a minute, no one said that. That's not my word, I didn't say that. Le'ul, did I call her a

163

bootlicker?

**Le'ul:** You didn't, I didn't hear a word like that. (*Both of them continue to stare at Letegergish. She does not know what to say or do next.*)

**Letegergish:** (*close to crying.*) All right. We'll see where all your smart talk and collusion will get you! (*She exits quickly.*)

**Le'ul:** (*laughing in amusement.*) Kidisti, you can be so naughty....

**Kidisti:** I swear to you! (*imitating the Cadre and Letegergish.*) Can you imagine me following her example? Am I now supposed to be called 'Sofia' and to answer, 'Yes Kelly?' (*The bell rings, both of them pick their respective netselas to go.*) Promise to explain to me this thing, this *'tewedibe'* and the association, I can't not do here what my sister is doing in Italy! All right, good night. (*She exits.*)

*Le'ul, fully dressed to go lingers at the exit and Mussie approaches her from another section.*

**Mussie:** How was your day? Am I late?

**Le'ul:** No, you are on time.

**Mussie:** (*searches the area with his eyes to make sure no one is listening.*) We don't have enough time. This week, a big operation has been planned right here in Asmara. Now, go straight to the usual house. Some of our people will be there—they will give you all the instructions you need. I'll tell you later exactly when and how the actual operation is to be carried out. We are now at the preparatory stages. Take some pam-

164

phlets from the house and distribute them to the usual people on your way home. The operation I'm talking about is going to be big and dangerous. I don't need to mention secrecy. It's top secret.

Le'ul: Don't worry about that. Before you go, Kidisti wants to join us. Should I start the process? What do you think?

Mussie: No, no, wait. No need to hurry. Kidisti is sincere and innocent, but she's too explosive. She's giving Letegergish and the Cadre a lot of headache. Let's leave her like that for the time being. She has to understand first and cool down a little, before we do anything. What do you think?

Le'ul: All right, as you say.

Mussie: How is home?

Le'ul: Ah, I hope it continues like this. It looks like love and peace are about to reign.

Mussie: That's only the beginning. You'll see, Weldu is going to grow into something bigger. Patience, fortitude and courage is all you need. From now on, Le'ul, stop distressing yourself.

Le'ul: I won't, I've learned my lesson.

Mussie: All right, ciao.

Le'ul: Ciao.

*They exit in different directions.*

Arag, 1983

165

# The Other War

*Translated by Paul Warwick,*
*Samson Gebregzhier and Alemseged Tesfai*

First published in *Contemporary African Plays,*
Edited by Martin Barnam and Jane Plastow,
Methuen Publishing Ltd., London, 1999

**Characters**

*Letiyesus*, an Eritrean grandmother
*Astier*, her daughter
*Assefa*, Astier's husband, an Ethiopian cadre
*Hiwot*, an old friend of Letiyesus
*Solomie*, Astier's daughter from a previous marriage with an Eritrean
*Kitaw*, Astier and Assefa's son

## Act One

*The curtain opens and we see* Hiwot, *a woman of about forty-five,*
*moving around the stage. Center stage there is a table, covered with a*
*clean cloth, and chairs. To the left is a cupboard which contains glasses*
*and other household objects. On the right there is a radio cassette play-*
*er. On the left, by the entrance, there is a hat stand. The house is clean*
*and well-kept, it is the house of a middle-income family in Asmara.*
    *As the play starts,* Letiyesus, *a woman of around fifty five to sixty*

*enters slowly. Although she is tired, her movements seem distraught. She has come from her village. Leaving her bag by the door, she says, 'How are you, Hiwot?' while she arranges her netsela. Hiwot seems shocked but runs to greet her friend. Letiyesus is so happy to have come home that she doesn't notice that Hiwot seems disturbed.*

**Letiyesus:**   *(sitting on a stool, down stage.)* Oufff... Yesus, Mariam and Yosef, I'm so tired! On my way here I called in at your house but they told me you were here.

**Hiwot:**   Why are you late...did you come on the night bus?

**Letiyesus:**   *Mbwa!* I left this morning but because of all these checkpoints it took all day. Oh, what a terrible life...and those men at the checkpoints! Tell me, are they human beings, or animals? Shameless people! *(grabbing her breasts and imitating their voices and gestures.)* What have we got here...huh? What have you hidden here? They wouldn't spare anyone, even old women.

**Hiwot:**   You're lucky it stopped at that...*(She opens her mouth as if to speak urgently, but glancing furtively around the house she gets nervous and says nothing.)*

**Letiyesus:**   *(Not noticing Hiwot's behavior, she speaks despairingly.)* What can we do?

**Hiwot:**   How was the village? *(She begins to prepare coffee.)*

**Letiyesus:**   *(biting her lower lip and shaking her head.)* They are searching the heavens for a drop of rain. But there isn't any. Years ago, I remember, Mariam herself used to hear our pleas. She used to respond immediately. But now? I don't know what's wrong with her. On my way here—people must have thought I was crazy—I was arguing aloud, provoking her: *(looking up.)*

'What's wrong with you?' I asked her. 'Have you deserted us now? Are you taking sides with THEM?!'

**Hiwot:**     *(laughing.)* So, you've started fighting with saints as well?

**Letiyesus:**     *Mbwa!* My argument is full of love, not hatred. I was hoping that, from all the voices directed towards her, she would single out my own, as a mother would do at the cry of her own child. But, in vain! *(They laugh together.)*

**Hiwot:**     *(looking about her, she whispers.)* Have you heard anything about your son Miki-el?

**Letiyesus:**     Oh, the answer is always the same. 'He is in Sahel.' Then, when I ask how he is, *'Nebsi, nebsi!* He is fine, mother, don't worry.' That's all you ever get from these fighters!

**Hiwot:**     *'Nebsi?'* What does that mean?

**Letiyesus:**     *'Nebsi'* means... er...I think it means OK, good or something. But then they've changed everything: the way they speak, their hairstyles—do you know they have even changed our marriage ceremony?

**Hiwot:**     *(surprised.)* There were fighters marrying in the middle of your village?

**Letiyesus:**     Of course!

**Hiwot:**     Didn't they come?

**Letiyesus:**     *(sarcastic.)* Who, those 'lions' from the checkpoint? They are only brave around their own den. Listen, I'm trying to tell you about this wedding. The bride was wearing shorts right up to here *(She touches the top of her thighs.)* and her hair was curled like a hermit's, falling locks that covered half her face. A boy hardly older than them was to marry them. He said: 'Attention! Relax!' ... then *'Awet Nahafash!'* and that was that, they were married. In all my visits to them, I'd not seen a marriage before, I've never seen anything like it. I just sat there, stunned. It's amazing, times really are changing.

*Hiwot is laughing. Letiyesus continues her story, while going to remove her netsela.*

**Letiyesus:**   Then they started to dance, with their guns slung over their shoulders.

*Letiyesus demonstrates the way that fighters dance the cuda—they both laugh throughout. Suddenly, Letiyesus stops dancing. She has noticed that her house is not as she had left it. Things are rearranged.* Hiwot *immediately stops laughing. She looks nervously from side to side. She cannot look* Letiyesus *in the face. Letiyesus stands frozen and looks carefully around her home. The cheerful laughing has been succeeded by a heavy silence.*

**Letiyesus:**   Who has disturbed my home? Whose radio is that?

**Hiwot:**   *(avoiding the question.)* Please sit down, have some coffee.

**Letiyesus:**   *(sitting.)* Have those kebeles sent others to share my house?

**Hiwot:**   Not kebeles. The day before yesterday your daughter Astier came here with her husband and children. She demanded your key and I gave it to her. They moved into those two rooms and put all your things in the store outside. *(She avoids the angry glare of Letiyesus by*

*fiddling with the jebena and cups.)* He has been transferred from Addis Abeba. They both said that they
wanted to live with you, their mother.

Letiyesus: *(staring at* Hiwot, *shocked and angry.)* How can this be,
Miki-el's home becoming a shelter for an Amhara?
Why didn't you tell them that you didn't have the key?

Hiwot: I thought Astier was alone, that's why I gave it to her.
I didn't know he was with them. Later, I came to
speak with her and I heard them saying: *'Anchi manch
anchi manchi!'* I couldn't believe my ears. Since then,
I have left my house every day and waited for you
here. I wanted to warn you.

Letiyesus: *(Unable to control her feelings, she closes her eyes and
shakes with rage.)* Oh, wicked daughter! What will
people call me now? Whose mother-in-law? Some
enemy! Some Amhara!

Hiwot: *(consoling her.)* Please, please, my sister. Letiyesus calm
down, put it out of your mind. After all, he seems like
a kind boy, he's always smiling...

Letiyesus: *(shouting.)* There's no such thing as an Amhara who
doesn't smile. Nonsense! Even at the checkpoints,
they were grinning and smirking while they groped
and pawed us. *(pointing to her breasts.)*

*There is a noise outside and they look at each other.*

Hiwot: Here they come. *(she puts her hand on Letiyesus's shoulder.)* Please Letiyesus, my sister, hide your feelings and
show them a happy face.

Letiyesus: *(not listening, but looking to the heavens.)* Oh, Mariam.

what evil have I ever done, what is my sin?

*A girl, fifteen or sixteen years old, enters first, followed by Astier with a baby, and then Astier's husband, Assefa. The girl, Solomie, runs to her grandmother and hugs her while she remains seated.*

**Solomie:**   Grandma! Grandma!

**Letiyesus:**   Let me stand, let me stand. *(She looks at Solomie and joy spreads over her face.)* Oh my child, you have grown. *(She looks her up and down.)* Oh Solomie, my grandchild, I think you are destined to be short for ever.

*Astier and* Assefa *are waiting to be greeted, but Letiyesus does not turn to face them. This makes Hiwot uneasy and she shuffles around the stage.*

**Astier:**   I think that's enough for you Solomie, now it's our turn to be welcomed, Mother.

*Unwillingly, Letiyesus greets Astier with insincere kisses. She doesn't kiss Assefa, but shakes his hand. He holds her hand with both of his, bowing his head respectfully.*

**Assefa:**   *(still bowing.)* Endemin Allu, *Em-Mama*. Endemin Allu?

**Letiyesus:**   Dihan, Wedei, Tsibuq. I'm well, and I have God to thank for it. *(She goes to offer Assefa a seat.)*

**Assefa:**   No, no, no, I'll do that, please sit down, *Em-Mama*. *(He arranges the seats and they all sit down.)* Endemin Allu? *(then he speaks to Astier.)* Oh, she looks nothing like her photograph, in real life she is more beautiful and younger. Wait a moment, is this your mother or your sister?

*There is no answer, a heavy silence fills the room.*

**Astier:**   Did you understand him mother? He said that you are
young and beautiful. He thinks you look more like my
sister than my mother. *(She laughs uneasily.)*

**Letiyesus:**   *(unconvinced and with a tinge of sarcasm)* Really? May
be he is trying to flatter me. Your mother is old
enough, girl.

*Again there is uncomfortable silence. To break it, Hiwot moves things
around noisily.*

**Hiwot:**   He is right you know. You are still young.

*No one responds to her attempt to make conversation. She feels even
more uncomfortable and returns to her fidgeting.*

**Assefa:**   *(to Astier, in Amharic.)* I think she's tired, when did
she get home...how do you say that in Tiginya? Me-as
Metu... Gebu...

**Astier:**   *(helping him.)* Me-as Atikhen?

**Assefa:**   Good! Ma-as Atikhin?

**Letiyesus:**   I arrived just before you.

**Assefa:**   *(standing, anxious to escape the uneasy gathering.)* No
wonder she looks tired. I am tired myself. I want to
get some rest. I'll leave you two to carry on chatting,
you have a lot to catch up on. *(He goes into the next
room.)*

**Astier:**   Solomie, fetch him some warm water for his feet.

*Solomie obeys reluctantly.*

**Hiwot:**     Well, I think I'll have to go back too. My house has been locked up all day.

**Astier:**     Why don't you stay with us Mother Hiwot, let's have dinner together.

**Hiwot:**     No, I must go, it's getting late. *(to Letiyesus.)* Besides, I think you have missed your daughter and I should give you a chance to be together. Goodnight. *(She gets up to leave.)*

**Letiyesus:**     Goodnight, Hiwot, goodnight.

*Silence.*

**Astier:**     *(looking at the baby, then at her mother.)* Mother, aren't you going to look at Kitaw?

**Letiyesus:**     And what is Kitaw?

**Astier:**     Our son! It's not just Solomie any more, I have a son, Kitaw.

**Letiyesus:**     *(very insincerely.)* Oh, how forgetful of me! Of course I'll see him. *(Astier offers the baby to her mother. Letiyesus doesn't move from her seat, but just glances briefly at the child and then leans back. She picks up a cup of coffee and starts to drink it.)* Yes, a handsome child, what did you say his name was?

**Astier:**     Kitaw. Assefa chose the name. In Amharic it means 'punish them'.

**Letiyesus:**     *(irritated.)* And who does he intend to punish ?

**Astier :**     *(still looking at the baby.)* What about all the secessionists?

174

*Letiyesus cannot control herself, she throws the cup to the floor.*

Astier:      Mother, why did you do that, aren't you happy that
             we have come here?

Letiyesus:   *(angry, heavily sarcastic.)* Oh yes, I'm glad. My child
             and her children are with me again and I am very
             happy.

Astier:      But only your words sound nice. Your face says some-
             thing else. From the moment we stepped into this
             room you have been wearing this gloomy face that is
             making me uneasy. What wrong have I done you?

Letiyesus:   *(still slightly sarcastic.)* Me? You haven't done me any
             wrong.

Astier:      *(smiling.)* So, why don't you joke and laugh as usual?
             *(She nods her head and smiles knowingly.)* I know what
             you're thinking, Mother. I know your heart, too.
             You're angry because I married an Amhara. But Assefa
             is not like the other Amharas. He's kind and besides,
             he is a brilliant cadre. In time, as you get used to him,
             you will grow to like him. *(She laughs uncomfortably.)*
             He is so funny...you will see...you will not miss your
             son, Miki-el any more.

Letiyesus:   *(Unable to control her anger any longer, she erupts.)*
             Remember Miki-el is the same Miki-el who is your
             own brother.

Astier:      Yes, that's what I am trying to tell you. Assefa is not
             just a husband to me. He is also like a brother. In the
             same way, he will be like a son to you.

*Letiyesus stares at her daughter, amazed. She cannot think of anything
to say, feeling her daughter is lost to her. She remains silent.*

*Unconcerned, Astier continues to rock the baby. Enter Solomie.*

**Solomie:** Mama, Gashie Assefa wants you.

**Astier:** *(Holding Kitaw tightly to her, she gets up.)* I'm coming Assie.

*Exit Astier, Solomie and Kitaw.*

**Letiyesus** *(Staring at Astier until she is out of sight, she addresses the audience, very agitated and confused.)* Gashie...Assie...am I dreaming?

## Act Two

*The same room except there is now a telephone near the table. Two months have passed and the newcomers have had an effect on the family's life. Letiyesus is forced to cook, take care of the children, etc. We see Letiyesus sweeping the floor, folding the children's clothes and performing the daily household chores. On the wall is a banner bearing the slogan of a Dergue campaign for a conservation program. Solomie sits at the table and does her homework.*

**Letiyesus:**  Solomie, my child, please come and help me fold these clothes.

**Solomie:**  OK, Grandma, just let me finish what I'm doing.

*Letiyesus is arguing to herself and gesturing with her hands. Solomie sees her and leaves her writing to go towards her.*

**Solomie:**  Grandma, why are you always talking to yourself?

*Letiyesus and Solomie begin folding up sheets together.*

**Letiyesus:**  *(smiling.)* I am not talking to myself.

**Solomie:**  So who are you talking to?

**Letiyesus:**  To Mariam. I'm asking her to keep my grandchild Solomie safe and to help her with her studies.

**Solomie:**  *(laughing.)* Grandma, don't treat me like a child. How can you be praying when you are in such an angry mood? *(frowns seriously.)* You know, sometimes I do the same thing—I talk to myself like you do.

**Letiyesus:**  *Mbwa!* You little brat! However could you be talking to yourself like I do? You are too young!

| | |
|---|---|
| **Solomie:** | But Grandma, I have no one to talk to. *(She starts crying.)* At school nobody will come near me, the other students all chat together, but when I try to join in they walk away and leave me on my own. They have even given me a nickname. |
| **Letiyesus:** | What nickname? What do they call you? |
| **Solomie:** | 'Chairwoman's daughter.' |
| **Letiyesus:** | *(consoling her.)* So, what is there to be upset about? Isn't it true? Hasn't your mother become Chairwoman of our kebele? |
| **Solomie:** | Don't try to fool me. I saw you the day she was elected. You were so mad, you had one of your headaches. You even had to tie a band around your head. |
| **Letiyesus:** | *(pretending to hit her.)* Little girl, you are going to cause me plenty of problems. Never repeat what you have just said. Go now, go and finish your ho-wek. |
| **Solomie:** | Not ho-wek, it is homework. Anyway, I've already finished it. *(She sits on a stool near Letiyesus and looks her in the face.)* Grandma, Aya Miki-el...what does he look like? |
| **Letiyesus:** | *(frightened, but touched.)* What? How do you know about Miki-el, why do you ask about him? |
| **Solomie:** | I only want to know what he's like! |
| **Letiyesus:** | Tall, fair-skinned, handsome *(teasing.)* not like you! His teeth are chipped because he once fell over, playing with your mother when they were little. |
| **Solomie:** | You love him very much, don't you Grandma? |

178

**Letiyesus:** *(smiling tenderly.)* What do you think? I even love you, ugly little thing.

**Solomie:** Mama used to love him too. Whenever my father came home drunk and beat her up, she would say to me, 'If my brother Miki-el were here, your father would not dare treat me like this.' But after they divorced and she started seeing Gashie Assefa, she always spoke ill of you and Miki-el. She used to upset me so much. I hated here.

**Letiyesus:** Come now, Solomie. You are only a child. Aren't you taking on too much for someone your age?

**Solomie:** But what am I supposed to do or feel? Grandma, it is only here, in this house with you that I am laughing again. In Addis? *(pensively and reluctantly.)* When my mother and father were fighting, which was almost all the time, I used to hide under the bed so I would not see them. When he left us, she started to beat me just as he used to beat her. She really beat me, Grandma, and took all her anger out on me. Then Gashie Assefa came, actually he treated me quite well, but then neither of them were ever at home. They would go out, leave me all alone in a big house...I would feel lonely...so lonely, I would cry...Oh, how I cried, Gran...*(She cannot control her tears any longer and starts to cry.)*

**Letiyesus:** What are these tears for? *(She fakes hitting her again, with a spoon or a fan.)* I don't like tears and weepy weaklings. My nerves can't stand them.

*Solomie is full of remorse and hangs her head.* **Letiyesus** *is touched, she feels sorry for her and hugs her.*

**Letiyesus:** Oh, dear child. Shame on those who cause this suffering. Come, no more sadness, no more tears The time will come for you to be happy. Don't worry, the Virgin Mariam will not forsake us. (*She straightens out* **Solomie** *who, stopping her crying, wipes her eyes.*) Go on, finish your ho-wek.

**Solomie:** Not ho-wek, it's homework, Grandma!

*Letiyesus laughs and jokingly threatens her with a stick. Solomie giggles and is running towards the table when she suddenly stops and looks uneasy. Astier has entered, home from work.*

**Astier:** (*scowling at Solomie.*) Where is Kitaw?

**Solomie:** He's asleep.

**Astier:** Didn't I tell you to watch him even when he is sleep-ing? What if he wakes up alone and gets upset?

**Solomie:** Let me do my homework first.

**Astier:** What have you been doing all morning, chatting with her? (*meaning Letiyesus. She picks up the telephone.*) Oh, all this chatter (*dialing.*), hurry along, take your books to your room and do your homework in there.

*Exit Solomie.*

**Astier:** Ah, hello...Ato Zenebe? Good afternoon... Astier here...fine...look, there were four women who were late coming to the meeting today, we shall send them to you for punishment...Oh, take whatever measures you think necessary.

*Letiyesus has been listening attentively. Astier finishes talking, replaces the telephone and sits down near Letiyesus.*

**Astier:** How are you Mama?

180

| | |
|---|---|
| **Letiyesus:** | How are you Astier? Did you have a fine day? |
| **Astier:** | How could I have a fine day? These women are becoming a pain. |
| **Letiyesus:** | But it's only your second week on the job. Isn't it a bit too early for them to be a pain and for you to be dealing out punishments? |
| **Astier:** | No, no, no, no, *(Shaking her head and trying to persuade her mother.)* ...You don't understand, Mama. If we are to work effectively we must have strict control right from the start. If things are not set right now, they never will be. For your information, Adei Hiwot is among those to be punished. |
| **Letiyesus:** | *(confused.)* Hiwot? Our Hiwot? |
| **Astier** | Yes, Adei Hiwot herself. Why don't you come late to a meeting and see if you will be spared? |
| **Letiyesus:** | *(drawling, deliberately.)* If you are not worried about preparing your own meals, so be it, I'll accept your punishment. |
| **Astier:** | Meals cannot be a problem. We can all eat in restaurants. But what I simply cannot understand is how it is that you find plenty of time for coffee gatherings and braiding each other's hair, and have no time at all for meetings. This is simply unacceptable. |
| **Letiyesus:** | *(rubbing her forehead and eyes.)* Astier, my dear daughter, please listen to me. Let us, for once, try to discuss things calmly. Is this it? Are we to remain antagonistic as though we were not mother and daughter? |
| **Astier:** | Why do you think this is so, Mother? Well, I'll tell you. Our hearts are in different places. Yours is with |

Miki-el, and whether you like it or not mine is right here. I am right here and here I shall remain.

Letiyesus: *(shaking her head.)* How would you ever know what is in my heart? You frighten me, Astier, you truly frighten me...and nothing is more terrible than to be afraid of one's own child.

Astier: Why should you be afraid? *(With a dramatic wave of the hand.)* There's plenty of democracy here. You have the right to speak freely. Let's talk.

Letiyesus: *(picking up some courage and adjusting her dress.)* All right, then, listen to me. The fact that you are the chairwoman of this kebele would not have mattered to me. I know how the elections are conducted and I know a lot of good people are compelled to serve in such posts. I would have found some excuse for you too, I would have said that you were nominated, unwillingly elected...But, as soon as you sat on that chair, you overwhelmed everyone with your enthusiasm. You've been penalizing people, picking quarrels with everyone within your reach. How do you expect to benefit from fighting against your own family, your own people?

Astier: *(her face flushed with rage.)* My family? Who are my family and my people? Don't you realize that you and father, especially father, have left me with a scar *(touching her heart.)* I will never be able to get rid of, all my life?

Letiyesus: *(jumping up, uncontrollably angry.)* What? What did you say? You unfeeling, cruel child! Didn't your father raise you and your brother the best way he knew and shower upon you both the unselfish love that only he was capable of giving? Didn't he go through hell, sac-

182

rificing his own pleasure and fighting against the illness that finally consumed him in order to build this house, this shelter for you? How dare you desecrate his memory in my presence? There must be a limit even to my fear of you. Or have I totally lost you?

**Astier:** If you think you are losing me now, you are mistaken, Mother. Remember that day, when I was only a child, when I could not tell good from bad, when the taste of knowledge was still fresh in my mind...remember when you married me off to Zecharias? That's when you lost me. Yes, Mother, you and father gave me to a drunkard, just because his parents had money and some fancy titles. You didn't even notice that I was only half his age. Now, who are you to give me any advice?

**Letiyesus:** So you are settling accounts, are you now? One person, Zecharias, did you wrong and you are wreaking your anger on your own people in revenge? Have you no conscience at all?

**Astier:** *(shaking with rage and shouting.)* Conscience? What conscience? Listen, Mother. I was beaten up, trodden on by Zecharias so much that I thought it would never end. My face was constantly swollen. Look at the marks under my eyes. I spent my youth, lying in bed, crying endlessly, waiting for him to come back drunk and use or misuse me, as he saw fit. Now, Mother, you are asking me why I am so enthusiastic about these people here? And why shouldn't I be? Zecharias locked me behind bars, Assefa opened the door and my eyes to the world. My heart was full of hatred, Assefa filled it with love. I was ignorant, today I am a chairwoman. *(She puts her hands of her hips.)* Now, what do you have to say? Who are my people? You or them? Answer me...say something...I thought you wanted to talk.

**Letiyesus:** *(speechless, she cannot control her tears.)* I have no answer, my daughter. Nothing to say. Besides, am I not weeping? Aren't my tears enough?

**Astier:** The truth is bitter, isn't it, Mother? You can't swallow it. Why else would Letiyesus weep? Since when did you weep, Mother?

**Letiyesus:** But I shall weep! I am a mother! When I see you, my own daughter, choosing the way to destruction, to the abyss you are too blind to see, wouldn't my womb revolt? Wouldn't my motherhood scream? No, don't be under any illusions. It is not your 'truth' that's making me weep, Astier. You have no truth.

**Astier:** *(sarcastically.)* Really?

**Letiyesus:** Yes...and if you think you are going to find the truth among these unwelcome strangers, we shall see, Astier. *(drying her tears and speaking slowly, in measured tones.)* Time will show.

*Assefa arrives home from work and puts his coat on the table.*

**Assefa:** I'm hungry! I am starving!

*Assefa notices Letiyesus' eyes are red from crying. He seems shocked and looks from one to the other for an explanation.*

**Assefa:** *Endiye!* What's going on here? Is she crying? *(He kneels beside Letiyesus and puts his hand on her shoulder. She doesn't like this.)* What's wrong, *Em-Mama?* Why are you crying like a child?

**Letiyesus:** I'm all right, my son. It is my old migraine...it must be the smell of coal...just a headache.

**Assefa:**    *(to Astier.)* Another one of your quarrels? And what have you said to her this time? What kind of a person are you, anyway? Please calm down, *Em-Mama*. Are we to have no peace in this house? *(He takes Astier's hand and goes towards the door.)* Come into the bedroom. I want to talk to you about this.

*They exit and Solomie comes out of their bedroom. She goes to her grandmother.*

**Solomie:**    *(whispering.)* I overheard everything she said to you. But don't cry, Grandma. Tears don't suit you...I love you more when you are laughing and cheerful.

**Letiyesus:**    *(wiping her tears.)* You're right, Solomie. You're right, dear child. What's the point of weeping? Our tears give pleasure to the enemy. One day all this will change and Mariam will show me their misery. I know it, I feel it.

**Solomie:**    *(hugging her tight.)* That's how I like you. Your own daughter saying those terrible things to you! If I spoke to her like that, she'd kill me, she would.

*Astier appears from her room. Solomie stops talking and releases her grandmother from her embrace.*

**Astier:**    Get the lunch ready!

## Act Three

*The scene is the same as before. On the table there are empty bottles and unwashed glasses and plates. The house is in a mess as there has been a party. Letiyesus ties a cord around her head [traditional Eritrean cure for a headache] and after putting a cloth around her waist she reluctantly begins to tidy up. Enter Hiwot from outside. The banner on the wall is now about the 'Red Star' campaign.*

**Hiwot:**   Good morning, Letiyesus.

**Letiyesus:**   *(looking up.)* Yes, who is it? Ah, how are you Hiwot?

**Hiwot:**   *(looking at the mess in disgust.)* What is this? What's been happening here? It looks like donkeys have been let loose the whole night.

**Letiyesus:**   *(looking at the bedroom.)* Ssh, they are sleeping. Talk softly, they may hear us.

*Letiyesus pulls Hiwot downstage towards the fornello and they sit as Letiyesus prepares tea.*

**Letiyesus:**   You're right, my house was full of donkeys all night.

**Hiwot:**   What was the gathering for?

**Letiyesus:**   A party, another party. Every night, partying, drinking, brawling, dancing... but last night was something else. *(imitating their toasts and being funny about it despite her headache.)* 'Victory to the Red Star Offensive!' 'Yes, victory, victory!' Glasses of cognac down throats. 'Bandits will vanish! Yes, vanish, vanish' Glasses of whiskey into bellies. I am sheltering beasts in this house, my dear Hiwot.

**Hiwot:**   But what can you do?

186

**Letiyesus:**    What can't I do? I am not that desperate, you know. I sat here the whole night and condemned them to God, damned them all to hell. 'E…h! I said throughout the night. *(patting the floor [asking God to condemn someone].)* 'E…h E…h!' When they said, 'We shall triumph,' I responded, 'You'll be defeated,' and when they shouted, 'Destroy the bandits!' I said, 'You'll be destroyed.'

**Hiwot:**    *(laughing sympathetically.)* Poor Letiyesus! At least you consoled yourself, gave yourself some relief. These people thrive on crimes and sins, my sister. Your condemnation and damnation will not bother them.

**Letiyesus:**    I didn't do it to bother them. I was not addressing them, no. I closed my eyes and sent all my prayers and wishes straight to heaven, and I know they got there. These people will neither destroy us, nor win. The Mother of Christ is up there. *(Hiwot laughs.)* I am telling you, I mean all this. *(Letiyesus pauses for a while and then, recalling the previous night's events, shows her disgust.)* Oh, the frivolity, the immorality I witnessed last night. And the girls…*(she imitates their movements.)* … dressed in sickening colors, their faces covered in powder—up-and-down, in-out, swing-sway—Oh! *(She shakes with even more disgust.)* They brought on my migraine and here I am.

**Hiwot:**    *(trying to change the subject and half-whispering.)* What about Astier? Has she become one of them?

**Letiyesus:**    To tell you the truth, she is much better than the others. She is reserved, you know, none of the frivolity and immorality of the others.

**Hiwot:**    Ah, this is a mother talking, isn't it?

187

**Letiyesus:** No, the mother thing comes only when there is a child thing to match it, my dear Hiwot. My daughter has taken me out of her heart. She has closed the gates to me. She is driving me against her. But my womb, my motherhood fears this confrontation.

**Hiwot:** In fact, I came here to tell you about her, Letiyesus. Everyone in this kebele hates her and they are plotting against her. Every man and woman has already been fined and there is a rumor going around that she is taking kebele money for herself. She may even go to jail.

**Letiyesus:** So be it. Let her get what she deserves if that's the case. I have neither the intention not the inclination to stand up for a cursed child.

**Hiwot:** But consider this, if she goes to jail it will be all the worse for you. You will be stuck here, raising her son. No, I'll talk to her. Fall on my hands and knees and beg her to return to her senses.

**Letiyesus:** You'll lick cement, eat dust for nothing. Do you want to invite trouble onto yourself? As for her son, I am raising him whether she is here or not. So, what difference will your gesture make? Or do you want another penalty? Just pray that I shall be spared all this suffering.

**Hiwot:** *(standing to leave.)* All right then, as you wish. How painful for you to have such a daughter. How did she ever become so heartless?

**Letiyesus:** *(sitting and staring into the audience, half lost in thought.)* She always was a strong, stubborn girl, even when she was little. But I am afraid we also had some responsibility for what happened. After she gave birth

188

to Solomie, she told us she wanted to divorce
Zecharias. We would not hear of any such thing—her
father and I. She insisted, cried, screamed...but, we
forced her to be patient and look after her family. We
had no idea she would be driven to this, no idea whatever that someday she would betray her own country
and people.

**Hiwot:**     Let me go before they wake up. Goodbye.

**Letiyesus:**     Goodbye, Hiwot.

*Hiwot exits and Leityesus continues her work. Enter Solomie, from out-
side, carrying the child.*

**Leityesus:**     Where did you take that child in this cold weather?

**Solomie:**     I met a school friend and we were just chatting by the
door. *(She kisses the child.)* Grandma, I overheard those
other children talking about fighting in Sahel. They
said that a lot of *tor-serawit* were killed. Are you listening?

**Letiyesus:**     *(scolding.)* Nosy child! You have no business listening
to other people's conversation.

**Solomie:**     They were talking right next to me!

**Letiyesus:**     *(interested.)* So, who did they hear this from?

**Solomie:**     From the radio of the fighters. From *Dimtsi Hafash.*

**Letiyesus:**     Wo...If you repeat that again, they will strangle you.
Nowadays, even your Gashie is hostile towards you. I
can see it in his eyes.

*Assefa comes from his room, wearing pajamas. He rubs his forehead with his right hand: he has a headache. Slowly he pulls up a stool and sits with Letiyesus. Solomie, carrying the child, moves around the room.*

**Assefa:** *(to Letiyesus.) Em-Mama*, how are you this morning?

**Letiyesus:** Fine, thank you—and you?

**Assefa:** Ouff, I have a pain in my head... Hey Solomie, give me two of those aspirins over there.

*Solomie brings the aspirins and after Leityesus hands him some water, he swallows the pills. Astier enters in her nightgown.*

**Astier:** *(kissing her son.)* Has he eaten his breakfast?

**Solomie:** Yes, early.

**Astier:** What time is it? *(She looks at her watch.)*... Oh, ten o'clock. *(Moving towards Letiyesus.)* It's a good thing that today is Sunday. Good morning, Mother... Oh, those headaches, why do you tie your head up, didn't I tell you not to?

**Letiyesus:** *(holding her head between her hands)* Oh, I feel like my head will burst and this pressure helps it.

**Astier:** *(laughing, to Assefa.)* This is known as Letiyesus-ism around here.

**Assefa:** Bakishin... Stop your little jokes.

*Letiyesus is pouring tea and ignoring them.*

**Assefa:** *Em-Mama*, could you warm some water for my feet?

*While Letiyesus puts a container of water on the fire, Astier whispers something to Assefa and he nods his head, he seems impatient to speak to Letiyesus while she works. He drinks tea and then speaks eagerly and passionately to Letiyesus in broken Tigrinya.*

**Assefa:** *Em-Mama*, Astier and I want to talk to you about Mika-el.

*Letiyesus is so startled she drops what she is holding on the floor.*

**Assefa:** *(noticing her reaction.)* It's all right, it's all right. It's good news, don't be afraid.

**Astier:** Yes, Mother, he wants to tell you something good for Mike-el and for all of us. Just listen to him carefully.

*Letiyesus looks ready to hear something bad.*

**Assefa:** The Revolutionary Army is annihilating the bandits. Mika-el is Astier's brother and this makes him my brother too. I don't want him to lose his life for a worthless cause. We have to bring him back here. Help us to do so.

**Letiyesus:** *(confused.)* What are you saying to me, my son?

**Assefa:** *(to Astier.)* Please tell her.

**Astier:** *(politely.)* Mother, what he's trying to tell you is about all of Miki-el's comrades. All the *gedli* are surrounded, they are in a critical situation. If you know where he is, or if you can send a relative to him as a messenger, tell him to surrender. Without being in any danger, or being harmed or imprisoned, he can come home to you. Mother, Assefa can do anything, everyone respects him.

**Assefa:** Yes, I can bring him to Asmara by helicopter.

**Letiyesus:** *(She despises their whole behavior, her headache gets worse and she presses here temples with both hands.)* How am I supposed to know where he is? I don't even know whether he is dead or alive, and I know of no relative who is in contact with him.

**Assefa:** Em-Mama, don't you want Mika-el to be here with us? *(She doesn't answer.)* Send a relative and try to contact him. *(Still no answer)*. Em-Mama, we are doing all this for your benefit, Endiye! *(He gets angry and moves closer to Letiyesus.)* Don't you feel sorry for your own son?

*Letiyesus is also losing her temper and she fidgets in her chair. Assefa's polite manner has disappeared and he starts shouting.*

**Assefa:** *Em-Mama*, your son will be eaten by vultures!

*Letiyesus looks Assefa full in the face.*

**Letiyesus:** Why don't you just leave me alone? What do you want of me?

**Assefa:** *(shouting.)* Your son will be eaten by vultures! VULTURES!

**Letiyesus:** *(angry.)* So he will be eaten by vultures! What of it? Is he any better than all his comrades?

*Assefa cannot believe what is happening. He glares furiously from Letiyesus to Astier. Solomie is standing behind Astier, still with the child in her arms. She is frightened and angry and she is biting her lower lip. Astier quickly tries to calm the situation.*

**Asteir:** Oh, Mother...

**Letiyesus:** You be quiet, too, I have a headache.

**Assefa:**     (*extremely angry, to* Astier.) Just ignore her! We are being too soft on this woman. (*pointing his finger* at Letiyesus.) It looks as if you yourself are a bandit, just like your son. (*He sits down scowling.*) You, Solomie, come and wash my feet!

*Astier is staring wildly at her mother. Solomie gives Astier the child and brings boiling water. Without adding any cold water she gives it to Assefa. Assefa and Astier are so involved with Letiyesus that they do not notice what Solomie is doing.*

**Assefa:**     (*muttering to himself in exaggerated agitation.*) I don't believe it! Such ingratitude! Pure arrogance! (*While he speaks he puts his feet into the water without looking.* Solomie *is at his feet, ready to wash. He screams.*) Aaah! This little bitch has burnt me! (*He slaps her face and she falls over.*)

*Letiyesus jumps up, but when she sees that Solomie is all right, she sits down on her stool again.*

**Astier:**     Are you OK, Assie? (*to Solomie.*) You idiot, you want to burn him with hot water? (*She kicks out at Solomie from her seat but she cannot reach.*)

**Assefa:**     (*almost speechless with pain and anger.*) Astier, bring me the water yourself. (*He heads towards the bedroom, looking malevolently at Letiyesus and Solomie.*) So, it's you and I now. So you are messing around with me? All right we'll see. You don't know what you're up against. (*He limps out.*)

**Astier:**     (*to Solomie.*) Get up, take the child.

*Solomie snatches her brother.*

**Astier:**     Careful, or I'll thrash you! *(While looking at Letiyesus, she pours cold water into the container of hot water.)* As if you haven't done me enough harm, are you now destroying my happy family? Do you consider yourself a real mother? You are even turning Solomie against me.

**Letiyesus**     Turning Solomie...I am turning Solomie against you? Aren't you giving her enough reasons to hate you for yourself. Can you point to a single moment when you gave her motherly love? Besides, not just Solomie, every person in this kebele is against you. They are all after you. Ask yourself where you are, where you are heading.

**Astier:**     Stop this, Mother! Stop provoking me! Stop cornering me or God knows what I'm going to do to you! *(She snatches up the container, spilling some water and goes towards the bedroom. She meets Solomie, who is carrying the child and anxiously listening.)* Out of my way!

*Exit Astier, Letiyesus and Solomie stay behind, looking at each other.*

**Letiyesus**     *(examining Solomie's cheek.)* Are you all right? *(Solomie doesn't answer, but begins laughing.)*

**Letiyesus:**     Why are you laughing, did you do that on purpose?

**Solomie:**     Yes, he had no right to insult you, calling you a bandit.

**Letiyesus**     *(jokingly putting her fingers round Solomie's throat.)* He'll strangle you like this. *(Solomie shrugs, Letiyesus looks at Kitaw in disgust.)* Ouff, what a nose. I hate noses like that.

**Solomie:**     No, he's handsome, Grandma.

| Letiyesus | *(going to her fornello.)* He doesn't look like us. He is not one of us. |
|---|---|

## Act Four

*The 'Red Star' banner has been replaced by a slogan about 'The Foundation of the Civilian Party' or something else that followed after the Sixth Offensive, implying that it has failed. Solomie cleaning the table and Letiyesus is sweeping the floor.*

| Solomie: | *(working.)* Grandma, who were those two women that I met at Mother Hiwot's house? When they met me they kissed and hugged me and one started to cry. |
|---|---|
| Letiyesus: | They are my sisters. The dark one was my cousin and the one who cried is my younger sister. |
| Solomie: | Adei Zaid? |
| Letiyesus | Yes, she's Zaid. |
| Solomie: | Because of Mama everyone hates us, even our family no longer come here. |
| Letiyesus: | No, don't say that. Nobody hates us. They were not crying because they hate us. It is just that they don't get the chance to see you as much as they like. |
| Solomie: | Grandma, you always treat me like a child who doesn't understand. But I think a lot and I know more than you realize. Why do women of this kebele frown whenever they see me on the streets? Because I'm her daughter, that's why. Nowadays I am starting to hate being in this house. I just feel like running away, disappearing. |
| Letiyesus: | *Mbwa!* Crazy girl, where would you go to? |
| Solomie: | To the field, to be a *Tegadalit.* |

**Letiyesus:** Ah, rubbish, child—it's only talk. When the first thorn pricks your foot you'll beg them to bring you back home.

**Solomie:** I would never beg to come home. *(Pause.)* Grandma, did Adei Zaid tell you anything about Miki-el?

**Letiyesus:** Must you bring this up every time? Why don't you simply keep your mouth shut?

**Solomie** *(stops sweeping.)* And why don't you tell me? Must you keep hiding things from me? I know a girl at school who tunes in to their radio, the *Dimtsi Hafash* every morning. She told me that thiry thousand *tor* have been killed. The Red Star Offensive has failed, the *tegadelti* have won, Grandma. I know you think about them all the time, that all your heart and soul is with them. I also realize that this is the cause of your quarrels with Mama. So, Grandma, I am not a child any more. I think, I know and I'm with you. Mama hates me because I am on your side. Now, Grandma, tell me, how is Aya Miki-el?

**Letiyesus:** *(Deeply touched, she puts her hand on Solomie's shoulder and looks her in the eyes.)* Oh, what times have befallen us, dearest Solomie? Girls your age are flirting around and here you are consoling me, caring and thinking. Oh, what would I do without you? *(She holds Solomie and strokes her hair.)* Miki-el is fine, he is alive and well. He has sent a letter and as you said, they have won a great...

*Assefa enters and they immediately separate. His face is dark with anger. He hangs up his coat, puts his pistol on the table and looks at them.*

**Assefa:** *(still standing.)* Continue to talk. Why do you stop? *(They don't answer.)*

196

| | |
|---|---|
| **Assefa:** | Solomie, come here. You stopped when I came into the room. Why? What were you talking about? |
| **Solomie:** | Nothing. |
| **Assefa:** | (shouting.) Speak, tell me the truth! |
| **Solomie:** | *(shaking with fear.)* Nothing, I was just telling her about my studies. |
| **Assefa:** | *(shouting.)* Does anyone talk about school while they are hugging each other? You were consoling each other, telling each other to be courageous. Isn't that so? |

*Solomie is frightened. Letiyesus goes back to her fornello and begins cooking.*

| | |
|---|---|
| **Assefa:** | *Em-Mama*, come here. (*She comes to him.*) |
| **Assefa:** | Please sit down. Solomie, go and look after Kitaw. (*She exits*). |
| **Assefa:** | *Em-Mama*, do you know where your daughter Astier is right now? |
| **Letiyesus:** | All I know is she left this morning. She said she had a meeting. |
| **Assefa:** | Didn't Adei Hiwot come round for a gossip as usual? |
| **Letiyesus** | *(calmly.)* Hiwot comes here to drink coffee, not to gossip. |
| **Assefa:** | Who are the worst gossips of this kebele? Who brings word of the terrorist *wenbedie*? |
| **Letiyesus:** | I don't know. |

**Assefa:** Isn't Hiwot one of them?

**Letiyesus:** Not when she is with me.

**Assefa:** *(moving slowly and menacingly towards her.)* What about you *Em-Mama*?

**Letiyesus:** I'm not that type of person, my son.

**Assefa:** Have you never met with *wenbedie*, *Em-Mama*?

**Letiyesus:** *(calmly, trying to pacify him.)* Listen, Assefa. Ever since you, yourself, told me that all the *wenbedie* have been destroyed, that my son would be eaten by vultures, I have given them up. How can I meet with those who are dead and destroyed?

**Assefa:** *(shaking his head and smiling.)* *Em-Mama*, you are a strong and cunning woman. You are no fool. *(smiling again.)* Sorry, *Em-Mama*, I was talking in anger...in this kebele many are jealous of Astier, she is a committed revolutionary, but lots of people are working against her. Do you understand?

**Letiyesus:** Yes.

**Assefa:** Now, although she is innocent, some people in the kebele have ganged up to accuse her of things she had nothing to do with. She is being held by the police for investigation.

**Letiyesus:** Are you saying she in prison? *(She doesn't seem to understand.)*

**Assefa:** Yes, that's why I am angry. That's why I said to you that there are some *wenbedie* in this kebele. They are smearing the names of committed revolutionaries by inventing false accusations.

Letiyesus: *(nodding her head pensively.)* So she is under arrest? Which station is she in? I must take her some food.

Assefa: There's no need to send her any food. I have spoken to the Colonel, he will release her. You think Astier will disappear that easily?

Letiyesus: *(standing, lost in thought and as if to herself)* I don't know, I just...don't know.

Assefa: Wait, *Em-Mama*, sit down. You felt nothing when I told you about her imprisonment. Had you already heard?

Letiyesus: No, I hadn't.

Assefa: Astier is your daughter, you don't feel shock or sorrow when your child is imprisoned.

Letiyesus: What will my shock and sorrow achieve? But she's my child and I'm obviously distressed by what has happened.

Assefa: But you are not sorry, you are not even surprised.

*Solomie enters, with Kitaw, but when she sees what's going on, she start to go out again.*

Assefa: Stay there, Solomie, stand still. *(She obeys.)* Listen *Em-Mama*, if Solomie was imprisoned you would pull your hair out.

Letiyesus: *(patiently.)* They are all my children and equal in my eyes.

**Assefa:** *(looking into her eyes.)* I don't believe you. If Mika-el was imprisoned you'd commit suicide, you'd hang yourself. Am I right? Eh, what would you do? What? What?

**Letiyesus:** *(fearless.)* I don't know, my son. I don't know what I would do.

*Assefa is furious again. He paces round the room slowly, looking in turn at Solomie and Letiyesus.*

**Assefa:** Well, I'll tell you what you' d do. You would die of sorrow. But Astier's imprisonment has not moved you one bit. Why? *(No answer.)* Because she is my wife? *(Silence.)* Or because she's a revolutionary? *(He bangs his fist on the table and points to Solomie and Kitaw, shaking with anger.)* They are both Astier's children. You love Solomie, but you don't care if Kitaw is alive or dead. Why?

**Letiyesus:** *(angry.)* I'm taking care of him, changing his nappies and messes. What do you mean, I don't care whether he lives or dies?

**Assefa:** *(pointing at Letiyesus.)* I'm not talking about nappies and messes. I am talking about love. The love you have for Solomie is obvious. I can read it in your face. But your heart has no place for Kitaw. Both of them come from your daughter's womb. Why is Solomie favored over Kitaw?

**Letiyesus:** If you have something else in mind, say it straight. I am not a child to sit here and be interrogated as to whom I love best.

**Assefa:** Why shouldn't you be interrogated? You think I don't

200

understand? Don't you know that I realize that you love Solomie more because she was born from your countryman? I'm not stupid. But you hate Kitaw because he is the son of an Amhara. *(sniggering.)* As far as you are concerned, everything that comes out of Eritreans is good, and anything mixed with Amhara is bad. Eh? Am I right?

**Letiyesus:**    These are your words, not mine.

**Assefa:**    *(hoarse and breathless with extreme rage.)* Em-Mama, I know what is in your mind and in the minds of all the mothers of the *wenbedie*. You send your children to the field and expect them to come back to you carrying a flag. But that is a dream. *Em-Mama*, a fantasy! Your son Mika-el and all his likes are gone...disappeared...exterminated. The new Eritrean generation is Ethiopian at heart. There is simply no place for *wenbedies* here in Eritrea. Don't waste your time, *Em-Mama*.

**Letiyesus:**    *(calmly, but with a touch of irony.)* I'm always here, I always have time. It seems you're the one that's wasting time. You should be at work, you know.

**Assefa:**    *(looking at his watch.)* I will not leave until I'm finished...Let me remind you once again that your son Mika-el has been destroyed...he's gone! But Kitaw is alive and here. Your daughter, Astier, comes from that Eritrean womb you are so proud of. I, Assefa, planted my seed in your own daughter's womb. Kitaw was born. Kitaw walks on this earth, just like your Mika-el. My roots are firmly planted in Eritrea and no power can ever pull them up. So, get this straight. Eritrea no longer belongs to the Mika-els, it belongs to us, *(pointing at Kitaw.)* to the Kitaws.

201

*Throughout this discussion, Solomie has been following every sentence, reacting with fear, shock and surprise.*

**Letiyesus:** *(standing up confidently, looking at Assefa in the eyes.)* Good, I think I understand what you mean. We were so naïve that when you told us that the war was in Sahel, somewhere in the mountains, we used to believe you. But today you taught me a good lesson. So, another war is going on in our daughters' wombs? *(with mixed sarcasm and consternation.)* I thought you loved and embraced Kitaw as your son. I had no idea he was just bullets and bombs to you.

**Assefa:** Stop ridiculing me, I don't like...

**Letiyesus:** *(interrupting.)* I'm not ridiculing you, I'm not used to doing that. You forced me to speak.

**Assefa:** *(picking up his pistol.)* Enough! Everything has a limit. All the year, I tried to be a son to you. I waited for you to look upon me as your own, but you ignored all my efforts. At first I thought it was your mother love, maybe also some sympathy for Mika-el, that was keeping us apart. But I was wrong. It's not just love or a little sympathy—you are, yourself, a *wenbedie*! *(He gets still angrier.)* And you have won Solomie to your side.

*He threatens her with his pistol and she is frightened. Solomie holds the child tight and hides behind her grandmother.*

**Assefa:** Listen, *Em-Mama*, from this moment on, if you and Solomie do anything or go anywhere without my permission, you will pay for it. Assefa Jembere is not going to harbor *wenbedies* in his own house! *(Shakes his head and laughs. He inserts the pistol in its holster and puts on his coat, staring at both of them. The telephone rings and he answers.)* Hello...yes...how are you

Comrade Colonel...Tomorrow afternoon? What's wrong, Colonel? Is it that serious?...Is that so? All right, then. Let's meet in the afternoon...Yes, comrade, goodbye. *(To Letiyesus)* Astier will be released tomorrow. She'll be here in the evening. Until then, none of you is to leave the house. I won't be home tonight, don't wait for me. *(He exits.)*

**Letiyesus:** *(immediately.)* Please, Solomie, my daughter, put the child to bed and call Mother Hiwot quickly. I'll be waiting and packing clothes.

**Solomie:** Whose clothes are you packing? What are you planning to do, Grandma?

**Letiyesus:** Mine and yours. Hurry up...we have to leave while we still have time.

**Solomie:** *(happy.)* Are we going to the village? *(Letiyesus nods. Solomie pauses, then apprehensively.)* What about Kitaw? What will happen to him?

**Letiyesus:** *(surprised.)* That's his business, we will leave him here

**Solomie:** How can you say 'That's his business?' Kitaw is my brother and besides he is only a child. I like him too, we must take him or I won't go.

**Letiyesus:** *(angry.)* Are you joking? Go and put him to bed now and call Mother Hiwot...

*Hiwot enters.*

**Letiyesus:** Oh, I was just telling her to call you, it's good you came.

Solomie *exits with the child.*

203

**Hiwot:** I was waiting for Assefa to leave. When he did, I thought you would be alone and I came. Why are you packing your clothes?

**Letiyesus:** I've had enough, my sister. I'm taking Solomie to the village .... From there? Only Mariam knows!

**Hiwot:** It's about time. You are a woman of dignity. You've put up with them far longer than you should have done.

**Letiyesus:** But today, he surpassed himself. He pointed his pistol at me and said 'The seed I planted in your daughter's womb has given us Kitaw. This land does not belong to Mika-el. It's mine and Kitaw's ...' That's what he said.

**Hiwot:** *(scornfully.)* And what does he think having a child means? What a cruel thing to say! Has he no manners?

**Letiyesus:** Why should he have any? Why should he, Hiwot? He has this mare of a woman, who does whatever he wants, who gives us his Kitaws. What kind of creatures do we have here? *(pauses, then laughs, mockingly.)* Oh, you should have seen him. As if having a child is the ultimate in heroism, an act of special bravery, he puffed himself up and *(Hands on hips, she repeats his puffs and grunts.)*...It was ridiculous. What indignity, Hiwot? Like the lion whose mane has been shorn off, I felt naked...and all because of her.

**Hiwot:** You are still respected, your honor and identity are still intact. I wish everyone could be like you.

**Letiyesus:** Oh, you've made me forget my business. Solomie! Solomie! *(Solomie does not appear. To Hiwot.)* I am in a dilemma. She is insisting that Kitaw goes with us. She's adamant.

| | |
|---|---|
| **Hiwot:** | Solomie said that? |
| **Letiyesus:** | Who else? Please my sister Hiwot, tell her we can't. |
| **Hiwot:** | *(thinks for a moment.)* Letiyesus, why don't you take him? |
| **Letiyesus:** | You, too? Are you mad? I have burned inside because of this child—and now you want me to take him! If I have to bring him up, I might as well do it here, you know. |
| **Hiwot:** | *(holding Letiyesus' hand and speaking with a great deal of feeling.)* Don't block your mind. Think, Leityesus. He told you he is going to rule this land through his son, didn't he? He dared to say to you that this land belongs to Kitaw, and not to Miki-el. Will, then, brace up! Take the child away from them. Snatch him, Leityesus. He is your flesh and blood too. Burn them inside, just as they burned you. Don't let them use our own wombs to rule us! |
| **Letiyesus:** | *(looking at Hiwot with amazement. The whole idea is new to her.)* Mbwa! I honestly wouldn't mind burning them, breaking their hearts, as they did mine. But, it is a strange thought...too much for me, now...no, they'll murder us all. |
| **Hiwot:** | *(passionately.)* Come, Leityesus. Once you are out in your village and disappear with our children fighters, these people won't find you. Your sister Zaid will go now and take the child with her through the checkpoint on the Dekemhare road. You, Solomie and I will go by Adi Segdo, then we meet at Ala. Let's pack quickly. *(excited.)* When they return and find the house empty, they will fight each other! |
| **Letiyesus:** | *(grabbing Hiwot.)* You are not leaving on my account, where will you go? |
| **Hiwot:** | What do I have here except two or three *jelebia*? No, for |

better, for worse, I'd rather live with my brothers in the village. Anyway, if I stay here they'll make me pay for having been your friend: question me, maybe put me in prison. Don't you worry, I have nothing to leave behind here. Let me go, don't delay me. *(She exits.)*

*Letiyesus is thinking hard, when Solomie enters from her room and looks at her expectantly. Letiyesus glances at her.*

**Letiyesus:**   Why do you stand there, go and pack the baby's clothes.

**Solomie:**   *(very happy.)* Oh, Kitaw's clothes?

**Letiyesus:**   *(with a glimmering of a smile.)* Don't you 'Kitaw' him! Don't ever call him Kitaw again. Call him 'Awet'... that means victory, you know...Awet.

*Solomie jumps up and down with happiness and kisses Letiyesus, who pushes her away, muttering inaudible words, like 'Go, go' or 'Don't be a nuisance!'—all in good humor. When she is alone, she goes center stage and searches the skies.*

**Letiyesus:**   I don't know what you're saying about all this, Mother of Christ, but I am doing what I think is right. Help me!
*(She goes back to packing and exits with her packed bags.)*

## Act Five

*Astier and Assefa are sitting by a table. The latter, in his shirt with his collar undone and his tie loose, is on the telephone. Astier is sitting at his side and seems very anxious. The atmosphere is very tense. Their speech and actions reflect anxiety and depression.*

**Assefa:** Hello...Ato Berhe...Good evening! This is Assefa Jembere...Have you heard anything about them? It's been four days since they left now! OK, I'll wait for you to make contact...please...God keep you! *(He hangs up and looks at Astier, speaking in a desperate tone.)* He says he has sent someone to Dekemhare. He'll call as soon as he gets word.

**Astier:** *(her voice is sad and weak.)* If he sends a messenger to Dekemhare, we shall get the reply soon. If she went straight to our village we shall bring her back easily, it is near Dekemhare. What I'm afraid of is... *(She stops and cracks her knuckles.)*

**Assefa:** Why are you saying that over and over again? What are you afraid of? What is the reason for your fears? Do you know something? Do you suspect anything? Speak out! I want my son right here!

**Astier:** *(fearful and pleading.)* Please, Assie, don't you think I want my child back too?

**Assefa:** I don't know, everything is confusing me.

*He shakes his head and looks at her, with wide eyes, full of suspicion and hate. She watches him, afraid. The heavy silence is broken by the ring of the telephone. Both go to pick it up, but Assefa gets there first.*

**Assefa:** Hello...Major...How are you today...nothing? All right...thank you, Major.

*He slowly hangs up, staring at Astier, then bangs his fist on the table. Astier is startled. He says nothing and exits to his bedroom. Astier gets up slowly, clutching her abdomen. Fear, frustration and depression can all be read in her face. The telephone rings and, scared, she runs to answer. Then she stops, afraid, and stares at the telephone. Finally she gets up enough courage to pick it up.*

**Astier:** *(with a stressed, broken voice.)* Hello Aya Berhe...Yes, this is Astier. Really? Aya Berhe, he didn't succeed...Did he call you? So what did he say? Where are they? At Ala? *(She wants to cry.)* What about Kitaw? Is he with her? *(She controls her tears.)* ... What is she doing in Ala?

*Assefa enters, smoking a cigarette. Seeing her state, he controls his rage and stands in front of her.*

**Astier:** So Aya Berhe, couldn't they bring them back? *(She is greatly shocked by the response, which shows in her face. She lets the telephone fall and is silent, eyes closed.)*

**Assefa:** *(Snatching the telephone, he hangs up and breathes heavily.)* What did he say? Can't you speak?

**Astier:** *(Trembling, she has to lean on the table to support herself. She speaks in a low voice, sad and scared.)* My relatives met her...she will not come, Assie. She has...she's taken Kitaw and Solomie and crossed over...to them. She's going to Sahel, to join the *wenbedie*. *(Her voice fades away and she sits because she can no longer stand up.)*

*Assefa, bewildered and unable to believe what he has heard, holds his cigarette with his right hand and inhales a lungful. With the forefinger of his left hand, he points at Astier and shaking it threateningly, he squints.*

208

**Assefa:**    It cannot be possible. This cannot be happening.

*Astier looks up at Assefa, who regards her with hatred and suspicion, which frightens her even more.*

**Asteir:**    Assie, why are you looking at me like that?

**Assefa:**    *(moving closer to her, pointing his finger.)* You knew about this?

**Astier:**    *(It is her turn not to believe what she has just heard)* How could I know?

**Assefa:**    *(enraged, throwing his cigarette on the floor and stamping on it.)* Why not?

**Astier:**    Assie, you are not going to suspect me now, are you?

**Assefa:**    How can I not suspect you? *(tressing every word, or counting with his fingers.)* Your mother, your brother, your daughter and now my son. *(Shouting.)* MY SON KITAW! They have all become *wenbedie!* How do you expect me to believe you?

**Astier:**    *(looking into his face and pleading.)* Assie, just calm down a little...please. They may have gone but I am here with you.

**Assefa:**    *(grabbing his pistol from the table and pointing it at Astier's forehead.)* With me, eh? You are with me? I don't know who to believe here. No, speak the truth before I spill your blood. The truth! Now!

**Astier:**    *(paralyzed with fear.)* Assie, I'm telling you the truth, I'm not lying to you. I have given my body and all I have to you. You opened my eyes and I have devoted my life to the revolution. If you shed my blood, you'll be shedding the blood of an innocent woman who loves you. Assie...please...Assie! *(She holds his arms with trembling hands.)*

**Assefa:** *(shaking her hands off and loading his pistol.)* Don't touch me!

*He aims the pistol and Astier freezes. Holding her cheeks with both hands and pressing her temples with her fingertips, she awaits her death in absolute panic.*

**Astier:** *(weak with fear)* Oh, dearest mother, what have I done to you to deserve this?

**Assefa:** *(changes his mind and lowers the gun.)* No, death is all too quick and simple. Don't even think of leaving the house. I'm not finished with you yet. I'll send a guard immediately. You are not to leave the house.

*Assefa straps on his gun belt and starts to leave. Astier follows him, pulling at his coat.*

**Astier:** Assie, Assie...don't leave me alone. Don't shut me out. I left my family and relatives for you. You are the only person I have. Assie, have pity on...

*Assefa interrupts her with a heavy blow. She falls to the ground.*

**Assefa:** Do I care?

*Astier follows him out with her eyes. She looks around the room, then at the audience. She looks everywhere. She starts pulling her hair out. Finally, she puts her head in her hands and cries bitterly, shaking all over. No one is there to hear her.*

# "The Other War" — An Afterword

The theme that "The Other War" deals with is often the subject of controversy. Unless read within the historical context in which it was written, the play may appear to stand against mixed marriages in general and against love and marriages between Eritrean women and Ethiopian men in particular. Indeed, many have criticized it from that angle. That, however, is not why I wrote it.

Although the story for the play was based on the actual experiences of an Eritrean grandmother, the characters, the dialogue and the events in "The Other War" are fictitious. The theme in fact originates from an event that has left a lasting mark in my mind.

In September 1969, the year I graduated from the Haile Selassie I University, I found employment at the Ethiopian Ministry of Finance. I stayed with that Ministry until May of 1970, when I went to the US for further studies. My boss, Mulatu Debebe, the Minister of State for Finance, was later to be shot by the Ethiopian military Dergue in that terrible massacre of Ethiopian officials in 1974.

In those few months under his service, I was introduced to the character and attitudes of Ethiopia's high and mighty of the Haile Selassie Era. I also got the chance to get a fair idea of how they thought and interacted. The event that left an indelible impression

211

in me and that was to move me to write "The Other War" came at
the end of my short fling as an Ethiopian bureaucrat.

In April 1970, Mulatu told me that I was to accompany him on
a trip to eastern Ethiopia. He was touring the region, he said, in
order to gain firsthand knowledge of how the Ministry was faring
out in the provinces. He was taking me along to take notes of practically everything he was to say and to help him write a detailed
report upon our return. So we went. It was a two-week trip that
took us to the Somali border and back and that included detours
into remote towns and military garrisons. I got to know governors-
general, customs officials, provincial finance chiefs or *bejironds* and
wretched tax collectors working under the meanest of circumstances.

Except for Mulatu, all the rest had never seen me. Neither could
they guess my origin since my name and manner of speaking did not
betray it. Because I had come with Mulatu, they must have assumed
that I was one of them. So, they were loose and uncharacteristically
unguarded with their remarks. I remember being surprised to note
that everywhere we went, those who met Mulatu as officials or for
lunch and drinks were Amhara, or claimed to be so. Thus, they were
always speaking the same language, with the same attitude and
assumptions.

Most of their conversation revolved around themselves and their
customs. The *qinie* and the proverbs of the Amhara and gossip about
the Imperial family and the aristocracy, I found, were their favorite
topics. I am sure all peoples are proud of their origins and culture.
That is natural. But I noticed that the image that my companions
had about themselves went far beyond normal love and pride in
one's roots.

"You know, according to the Amhara..." one would begin, and
off the rest of them would go, regardless the topic. Everyone would
make a speech. Since I was a listener, I remember laughing at some
of their gloating, being impressed by some of the information or getting plain bored by the endless anecdotes. We got to Jijiga, the main
town in the Ogaden, after having made several stops at several places
in Harar Governorate General.

I remember now that the Governor of Jijiga was a Colonel. I
regret that I cannot recall his name. After a reception and a lunch-

eon befitting a Minister and his entourage, the Colonel spread a huge map on a board and started to brief us on the situation existing in Ogaden. At the time, a state of emergency had been in place in the province and martial law ruled supreme. Ogadeni guerrilla fighters were active in most areas of their own land and security on the Ethiopian-Somali border was not reliable. Throughout our tour of Ogaden, our Land Rovers had to be escorted by army units, both from the front and the back. Even then we all felt uneasy and tense.

Anyway, at the end of his briefing, the Colonel explained that the situation in Ogaden was fragile. He also admitted that finding a permanent military solution to the problem had been proving illusive.

"These are a very difficult people," he declared. "Even if we were to weaken them militarily, I doubt that we will ever succeed in winning them over politically. Therefore, your Excellency," he said, addressing Mulatu, "Our policy now is to mix these people with those of the rest of Ethiopia. Only thus can we make them kneel before us."

He did not stop there. He went on to explain what exactly he had meant by what he had said. "Therefore," he went on, "We are stationing unmarried military and civil Amhara youths to this province and encouraging them to have children from the women of these people either through marriage or by coercion. We will thus change their composition...."

I left the meeting totally incredulous. My companions, on the contrary, seemed content with what they had heard. We were leaving Jijiga. The Colonel and his guards had wanted to see us off to the outskirts of the town. I rode in the second Land Rover, with the Chief Treasurer or the *bejirond* of the Governorate General of Harar.

On our way, we were passing several Ogadeni nomads, some of them asking for a ride. Almost all of them had curly, uncropped, unwashed and greasy hair falling to their necks or shoulders. Stick in hand and the inevitable dagger firmly sheathed to their waist, they were all quite a spectacle.

The *bejirond* stuck his head out the window of the Land Rover to study a sturdy youth we had just passed. "You see, young man," he said to me, "The Amhara has crushed all Ethiopians to submission, except for these people. You have no idea how arrogant they are." He then continued to explain how right and appropriate the Colonel's ideas about ethnic mixing had been.

I was not in a position to talk or to reply to him. But, I remember burning inside. I remember feeling ashamed and degraded. "So we are considered among those crushed by the Amhara," I kept saying to myself. Every time I said that, I remember getting angrier for being confined to self pity.

Above all, it was the diabolical nature of what the Colonel had so proudly declared as government policy that had totally astounded me. Here I was face to face with the cruelty and cynicism of alien rule going far beyond any attempts at the physical annihilation and destruction of its subjects. I had absolutely nothing against ethnic mixing resulting from love between individuals. That is my attitude today as well. I may advise lovers to be aware of some of the difficulties that cultural difference may cause in their marriage, but nothing more. But this experience literally rocked me to my foundations. I had never guessed that a whole government could be so evil, so mean, so base and so open about it.

The b*ejirond's* comments hurt even more. When he called that innocent Somali "arrogant", he was awarding the dignity of humbleness and modesty to himself and his likes. I could not swallow such insolence. In my later readings, I came across the saying that "those who oppress others cannot themselves be free", it reminded me of the *Bejirond*. A logic that accuses those who refuse to be crushed of arrogance can only be the absurd logic of rulers and colonizers, I said to myself.

What I found still more paradoxical was the fact that the *Bejirond* was totally unaware that he was turning logic on its head. He was a kindly man who shuddered at the evil doings of his fellow men. "Don't tell me that", he would moan whenever someone narrated a story of theft or murder. He would even press his temples in horror. A church was something he would not pass. He would command the driver to stop, get out of the car, trot to the wall of the church and kiss it with the passion of a believer. "Have mercy on me, Lord," he would murmur as he retook his seat. And yet, that very pious middle-aged man would support the rape of innocent Oromo and Somali girls so that the Ogaden would be filled with little half-Amharas. If piousness can exist within the context of sin, there it was.

A few days into our trip, some casual remark revealed my origin and identity. "There is no way anyone can tell, he has no signs on him," said the *Bejirond* staring at me. He was probably looking for little slits or scars on my eyebrows which some Eritreans have from some traditional practice that is supposed to protect the eyes from diseases. We were eating lunch. I noticed the chatter cooling down considerably. Suddenly, I had become an intruder.

The next day, we stopped at a scenic spot for a barbeque and an informal chat. Mulatu enjoyed telling jokes. We were laughing when, as usual, someone mentioned the word, "Amhara", but interrupted himself self-consciously. Mulatu must have sensed the unease. He called me by my name, examined my face and said, "When we say Amhara, we mean highlanders, Christian Ethiopians. The name includes Tigrayans, Gurages, Hamasiens... any Christian highlander. Don't get the impression that it has any other meaning, O.K.?"

I did not believe him, of course. I doubt also that he had expected me to accept his explanation, which I did not. Instead, the Colonel's "policy" settled into the depths of my thinking, my consciousness. I could neither forget nor forgive it. It became a permanent fixture, a grudge-generating fixture in my psyche.

In 1981, when I moved to the EPLF's Cultural Division to help develop drama, the urge to portray such a "policy" in a play became an obsession. It proved difficult and I had to tear up a couple of attempts.

Sometime in 1984, someone told me about a grandmother who had snatched her three grandchildren from their mother, to join the EPLF. The younger mother had divorced her Eritrean husband and father of the children, to live with an Ethiopian cadre. When she and her whole family, including a child born from the Ethiopian, moved into the grandmother's home in Asmara, the house was embroiled in squabbles that slowly took the shape of irreconcilable political differences.

I went to the EPLF refugee camp in Orota to see the old woman. Without telling her why I had come, I talked to her for a couple of hours and learned much about how the Ethio-Eritrean conflict was affecting every household. I was convinced that I had finally found the basis and the setting upon which my play would be fashioned. I went back to Arag and created the characters and the dialogue that became "The Other War." I was, of course, keen to remove the plot as far away from the actual story of the grandmother as I could.

When I wrote the play in late 1984, daily reports were coming in of young Eritrean girls being raped by Ethiopian soldiers or being forced into marrying them. Naturally, these acts of terror reminded me of that colonel's policy in Jijiga. I had no doubt that the theme of my play would be timely and, perhaps, timeless.

Thus, "The Other War" came into being. It had and still has everything to do with governments and colonizers that use sex and marriage as instruments of ethnic cleansing. It has nothing to do with love and lovers, no matter their origin.

# GLOSSARY

**Adei**
mother, also commonly attached to the names of older women.

**Akhudir**
children's game where one kicks another - the "donkey-kick".

**Amhara**
name of one of the major nationalities in Ethiopia. For long, it had been the most dominant political group.

**Amharic**
language of the Amhara.

**Anchi Menchi**
"anchi" means you (female gender). "Anchi menchi" makes fun of Amharic by Tigrinya speakers.

**Awet Nehafash**
EPLF slogan meaning "Victory to the Masses."

**Aya**
word of respect for an older brother, cousin or friend.

**Bakshin**
Amharic word meaning please to a girl or young woman.

**Barrista**
Italian for bar tender.

**Bejirond**
Ethiopian official, chief of the treasury.

**Beles**
prickly pears

**Bidho**
challenge

*Cinque minuti e basta*   Italian for "five minutes and finished."

*Cistercensi (Sitawyan)*   Catholic clergy of the order of San Bernardo.

*Cuda*   traditional Tigrinya dance.

*Dejazmatch*   traditional title meaning commander of a front

*Dergue*   shortened name of the Transitional Military Administrative Council of Ethiopia whose chairman was Mengistu Hailemariam.

*Dihan wedei, tsibuq*   Tigrinya for "Well, my son, good."

*Dimtsi Hafash*   meaning "Voice of the Masses," - name of the clandestine EPLF radio which started operating in 1979.

*E una vita canaglia*   "it's dog's life" — Italian.

*Emba Galliano*   an area adjacent to Villaggio Paradiso

*Endemin allu*   Amharic for "how are you?'

*Endiye!*   Amharic expression of surprise.

*ELF*   Eritrean Liberation Front. The pioneer organization that was organized in 1961. It is credited for having started the Eritrean armed struggle for independence.

*EPLF*   Eritrean People's Liberation Front. An off-shoot of the ELF, it grew to become the dominant organization within the

Eritrean revolution. The EPLF defeated the Ethiopian army in May 1991, to win independence.

**Injera**
a pan-cake shaped soft bread made of ground taff, millets, etc. Taff is a cereal that commonly grows in Ethiopia and Eritrea.

**Fedayeen**
Arabic word, clandestine revolutionaries working in towns under enemy control.

**Fornello**
a small metal stove filled with hot coals and used for boiling food, coffee, tea...etc.

**Gashie**
Amharic equivalent of *aya*, title of respect for older persons.

**Gedli**
struggle, trials and tribulations...a word with spiritual implications used to indicate the holiness of the struggle for independence.

**Grazmatch**
traditional military title, meaning commander of the left flank.

**Guaila**
traditional Tigrinya music and dance in which the *cuda* is performed.

**Gurage**
a nationality in Ethiopia known for its entrepreneurship.

**Hamasien**
a region in Eritrea in which the capital, Asmara, is found. Today, most of Hamasien is encompassed in the Central Region of Eritrea.

| | |
|---|---|
| *Harbenya* | patriot, also the name of an EPLF magazine. |
| *Hdmo* | an Eritrean traditional house with an oval-shaped roof constructed from neatly rowed branches of trees covered by layers of flat stones and earth. |
| *Jebena* | a small clay pot used for making coffee. |
| *Jelebia* | traditional dress of most Eritrean women. Moslem men also wear traditional Arab jelebia. |
| *Kebele* | the Dergue's administrative units both in the towns and villages. These were also means of government and party control through the cadres who headed them. |
| *Kebessa* | the highlands of Eritrea. |
| *Khalas* | "Enough" or "that's it", an Arabic word widely used in Eritrea. |
| *Kirbit* | matches. When a nickname, it indicates a quick temper. |
| *Kitcha* | traditional Eritrean bread harder than injera, made form wheat, barley...flour. |
| *Krar* | traditional stringed musical instrument. |
| *Ma dai lasci stare* | Italian for "Come on, leave me alone." |
| *Maestra* | Italian for mistress or forewoman. |
| *Manjus* | little (Arabic), commonly used during |

the struggle for younger or physically smaller people.

*Mbwa!*      A common Tigrinya utterance expressing different types of feelings and moods. The intonation decides the meaning.

*Membir*      teacher

*Nebsi*      literally, "soul", used by EPLF fighters to indicate good health and peace of mind.

*Netsela*      a traditional Tigrinya shawl, usually white but decorated at the hem. It is hand-woven at traditional looms.

*Oromai (Oramai)*      Italian for "Alas!"

*Ouzo*      popular drink in Eritrea.

*Pente or Coste*      common derisive reference to people of the Pentecostal faith by other Eritrean Christians.

*Red Star Campaign*      the Dergue's sixth and largest offensive against the EPLF, launched and defeated in 1982.

*Sahel*      region in Northern Eritrea where the EPLF had its base.

*Salve*      Italian for greetings or wishes of good health.

*Sciopero*      Italian for strike.

*Sha'ibia*     Arabic for "people's" or "popular", short name for the EPLF.

*Shankilla*    a minority nationality in Ethiopia.

*Shobere*     Tigrinya vulgarization of "Sciopero."

*Suwa*      traditional brewed drink popular in Eritrea.

*Strategic Retreat*  the retreat of the EPLF from the environs of Asmara and Massawa to its base area in Sahel, upon the large-scale intervention of the Soviet Union on the side of the Dergue in 1978-1979.

*Tedawibe*    bordered on.

*Tegadalai*    a derivation of the word *gedli*, meaning one who struggles or fights for freedom. It also means a patriot, but contains more meaning as there is a spiritual or religious aspect to it.

*Tegadalit*    female fighter.

*Tegadelti*    plural for *tegadalai*.

*Tewedibe*    organized.

*Tigray*     Ethiopian region sharing a common border with Eritrea; the people of Tigray speak Tigrinya.

*Tigrayan*    a native of Tigray.

*Tigre*     the people and language of the people of the northern Red Sea coastline and the northern and western lowlands of Eritrea. Tigre is the language closest to Ge'ez from which Tigrinya is also derived. Tigre, however, is a distinct language.

*Tomween*    Arabic for store.

*Tor serawit*    Amharic for armed forces.

*Trenta Cinque*    1935, referring to Italy's invasion of Ethiopia on that year.

*Villaggio Paradiso*    an area in the northern parts of Asmara.

*Wedi*    the son of

*Wedi Libi*    a football player and coach and one of the veterans of the Eritrean struggle forindependence.

*Wenbedie*    Amharic for bandit.

*Weyley*    a Tigrinya expression usually voicing surprise or indignation.

*Woy*    an utterance in response to someone calling —informal.

*Yesus, Mariam. Yosef*    Expression of appeal or relief by Tigrinya women, usually of the Catholic faith.